Ecology

Science of Survival

Ecology

Science of Survival

by Laurence Pringle

The Macmillan Company, New York, New York
Collier-Macmillan Limited, London

The Macmillan Company, 866 Third Avenue, New York, N.Y. 10022
Collier-Macmillan Canada Ltd., Toronto, Ontario

Drawings and diagrams by Margery Argano

Library of Congress catalog card number: 72–158171

Printed in the United States of America
1 2 3 4 5 6 7 8 9 10

For George Bush and Roy Gallant,
who helped me on my way

Contents

1

The World in a Web

The spider spun its web during the night. By morning, several insects were trapped in the sticky threads. The spider deftly wrapped them in its silk and stored them for future meals.

If you come upon such a web in the woods, you might pause to look at its beautiful pattern, then walk on. This time, take a moment and think about the spider, its web, and the world around it. How did the spider get here? Do spiders of this kind live only in forests? Why is the web six feet above the ground, instead of two or twenty feet? Might this have something to do with the temperature, the wind, or the kind of flying insects the spider prefers to eat? Do any animals try to eat the spider? What happens to the spider when rain or wind destroys its web?

The world of the spider seems to be more and more complex the more you think about it. You could probably spend a lifetime learning about this one kind of spider. In your investigations you would use information from biology, ethology (the study of animal behavior), chemistry, physics, geology, meteorology, and even astronomy. You would be studying the one science that uses information from all of the other sciences—*ecology.*

No one is sure when the word ecology was first coined, but German biologist Ernst Haeckel was the first to define it, in 1869. Ecology is the study of the relationships between living things and their environment. The term comes from two Greek words, *oikos* (which means "house" or "place to live") and *logos* (which means "study"). So ecology is the study of the "houses," or environments, of living organisms—all of their surroundings, including other animals and plants, climate, and soil.

Although the science of ecology is a new one, people have been studying ecology and applying their knowledge of it for many thousands of years. Prehistoric people had to know something about the ecology of wheat and corn before they could successfully raise crops of these plants. Theophrastus, an early Greek botanist, is sometimes called the "first true ecologist" because he was the first to write about plants in terms of their living places, or *habitats,* such as forest and marsh. The Indians of the North American plains knew a great deal about the ecology of the bison, on which their lives depended. Today we often use ecological knowledge without being aware of it; for ex-

Sioux Indians had to be "bison ecologists" in order to survive.
(Painting by George Catlin, Courtesy of the American Museum of Natural History)

ample, when we want to have a lawn in a shady place, we plant seeds of a kind of grass that grows well in shade.

For the most part, however, people do not think ecologically. When we see a bird or wildflower, our first question is: *What is it?* Most people are content to know the names of some of the living things around them in nature. Perhaps you are the sort of person who wonders further: *What does it do?* You may want to know the organism's role in its environment, and how it affects and is affected by other organisms. Ecologists wonder about the same things.

Although ecological knowledge has been used by people for thousands of years, ecology is one of the newest of the sciences. For many centuries, scientists concentrated on naming the plants and animals they discovered and on describing the structure of the dead specimens they collected. Gradually, as the question "What is it?" was more easily answered, scientists began studying the effects of the environment on living organisms. During the 1800s, for example, scientists investigated the effects of day length on bird migration and the effects of humidity on the development of insects. Hundreds of books were published on the behavior of animals and on the distribution over the earth of plants and animals.

Still, the emphasis was on individual organisms. In the late 1800s and early 1900s, however, scientists began to study *populations* of organisms, rather than individuals. About the same time, they realized that all of the populations of plants and animals in a certain area make up a sort of *community*, with different kinds of organisms having different "jobs" in the community. Studies of nature became broader and more far reaching. In 1935, the word *ecosystem* was coined to describe all of the living communities of an area, together with the nonliving parts of their environment. The earth is one huge ecosystem. Other ecosystems within it include forests, lakes, meadows, vacant lots, your back yard, a rotting log.

To know more about ecosystems is the main goal of ecologists today. Even though an ecologist may still concentrate most of his studies on one kind of organism, or

Ecosystems can be small or huge—a pond or a mountain range.

on one plant-animal community, his findings help us to understand the ecosystems that include that organism or community. The challenge of ecology is to understand how ecosystems "work" and how they change with time.

It is a great challenge. The workings of nature are not as simple as we would like to believe. People used to speak of a "balance of nature" where, for example, a change in the numbers of rabbits might cause a change in the numbers of foxes. According to the balance of nature, if rabbits increased, the foxes that preyed on them would too. If rabbit numbers dropped, then so would those of foxes.

The simplicity of this idea appealed to people. But there is no such balance in nature. In most ecosystems, there are many factors—living and nonliving—that affect the numbers of organisms. Only in very simple ecosystems, such as in the Arctic or in those created by people on farms and in cities, does nature often work like a simple balance.

The study of ecology reveals that nature, or any ecosystem in it, is like a complex web. The web of nature, however, is much more complicated than the spider's web pictured at the beginning of this chapter. A spider's orb web follows a regular pattern; with string, time, and patience you could make one yourself. The web of nature is not that simple. One ecologist has said of the world's ecosystem: "It is not only more complex than we think. It is more complex than we *can* think."

People are part of the world ecosystem, and have a great and growing effect on many other ecosystems. The increasing numbers of people are changing ecosystems all over the world. Some of the changes are small and local: a

Wastes from a North Carolina paper mill change a stream ecosystem.

house is built on a vacant lot; a highway slices through a forest.

Some changes are major: Long-lasting insect poisons such as DDT were spread all over the earth before scientists became aware of the deadly effects of these chemicals on eagles, ospreys, and pelicans. Lake Erie, one of the largest lakes in the world, is badly polluted and "dying" as a result of wastes produced by people. The burning of coal, oil, and other fuels has affected the entire atmosphere of the earth; and dust particles in the air have helped reduce the amount of sunlight reaching the earth's surface.

Changes like these, along with thousands of smaller ones, have alerted us to the dangers of altering ecosystems before we understand the effects of the alterations. We fancy ourselves to be rulers of the earth. *But we don't know the rules.* The study of ecology may help us to learn the "rules of nature" on which our survival depends.

More and more, people are turning to ecology and ecologists for advice on how to live with nature without destroying our life-giving environment. But often there are no answers, or only partial answers. Ecology is a new science and ecologists know little about most of the world, especially about the tropics and the oceans. Some of the ideas of ecology, accepted for many years, are now being challenged and changed.

One example is the classic story of the Kaibab deer herd, which you will find in almost every book about ecology. According to the story, in 1907 there were about 4,000 deer on the Kaibab Plateau in Arizona. Then people killed most of the wolves, mountain lions, and coyotes that preyed upon the deer. The deer herd increased tremendously; by 1924 it totaled 100,000 animals. The deer destroyed or damaged most of their food supply and, in two successive winters, more than half of them starved to death. Numbers dropped still further in later years, finally leveling off at about 10,000 deer.

The story of the Kaibab deer herd was often retold because it was a good illustration of what happens when natural controls on deer numbers are eliminated. However, in 1970 a New Zealand zoologist named Graeme Caughley published an article in the journal *Ecology* that challenged the facts and conclusions of the Kaibab case. Instead of accepting what he read in books, he had investigated the original reports of observers at Kaibab. He concluded that the estimates of deer numbers were inconsistent and unreliable. Deer numbers did drop sometime in the span of 1924 to 1930, and the decline was probably preceded by a period of rising numbers. "Any further conclusion is speculative," wrote Dr. Caughley. Furthermore, he pointed out that the rise in deer numbers, whatever it was, coincided with a big drop in the numbers of cattle and sheep that were allowed to graze on the Kaibab Plateau. With fewer livestock present, there was more food for deer. This factor alone might have caused an increase in deer numbers. There was no evidence that the rise was caused by a drop in the numbers of wolves and mountain lions.

The facts of the Kaibab case will never be known. Because of this, it has to be discarded as a seemingly good example of an ecological idea. In the fast-changing science of ecology, many other ideas are being challenged and revised. Nevertheless, there are some discoveries about how nature "works" that aren't likely to change much with time. These basic ideas are presented in this book. Knowing about them, you may begin to sense that humans and all of the rest of nature are tied together in a complex but fascinating web. The study of that web is ecology.

2

Ways of Life

Set a jar of water on a window sill. Put some pond plants and pollywogs in it. You have an ecosystem—a recognizable unit of nature with living and nonliving parts. It is incredibly simple, of course, compared with an ecosystem like the great Amazon rain forest.

Any ecosystem is made up of two parts: nonliving (the physical environment) and living (the biological community). The nonliving environment usually includes energy from the sun, temperature, water, gases in the air, wind, soils, and the rocks beneath them, and the topography, or shape of the land. These nonliving parts of the ecosystem determine the kinds of life that can exist in an ecosystem, and they also affect each other.

Living things are affected by such nonliving factors as the amount of sun energy, the temperature of the water and the gases dissolved in it.

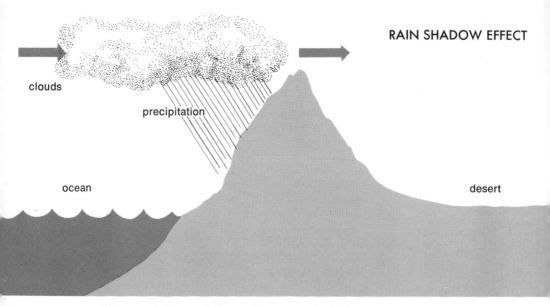

RAIN SHADOW EFFECT

clouds

precipitation

ocean

desert

Most precipitation falls on the seaward side, leaving little moisture for the land beyond the mountains.

The world's deserts, for example, occur where the annual rainfall is ten inches or less. This lack of rain is sometimes caused by topography. Along the west coast of North America, winds carry water vapor inland from the Pacific Ocean. The air is forced to rise as it hits the coastal mountain ranges. As it rises it cools and the water vapor in the air falls as rain or snow on the seaward side of the mountains. As a result, there is little rainfall on the other side. This is called the *rain shadow effect.*

In the Cascade Mountains of Washington, the annual precipitation may reach a hundred inches. Beyond the Cascades, in the Columbia River valley, the annual rainfall is about nine inches. So the topography has a tremendous influence on the amount of water that falls on the land. This, in turn, affects the plant and animal life. The rain-rich western slopes of the Cascades are covered with dense forests. In the rain shadow on the other side of the mountain range, only sagebrush, bunch grasses, and other desert plants grow.

The living parts of an ecosystem often affect the non-living parts. When rain falls on a forest, the tree branches and leaves help break the force of the drops. Layers of dead leaves on the forest floor soak up water and prevent the drops from washing soil away. Little water runs off the land. So the living trees help maintain the soil on which they depend. In fact, the trees add to the soil, since the leaves that fall to the forest floor eventually decay and become part of the soil itself.

Soils offer the best example of how nonliving and living parts of an ecosystem affect each other. Soil is made up mostly of grains of minerals, such as silica and clay, that are freed as rocks slowly break down. Spaces between the mineral particles are filled with air or water. Roots reach down into the soil, changing it physically (by loosening packed particles) and chemically (by withdrawing minerals). Dead parts of plants and animals are brought deeper into the soil by earthworms and other soil animals. Thousands of organisms live in a handful of soil. Most of them are too small to be seen, but they all affect the soil by taking minerals from it and adding wastes and their dead bodies to it. Soils are of special interest to ecologists because the lives of nearly all land organisms, including humans, depend so much on them.

*Earthworms affect soils by mixing
bits of leaves with the mineral particles;
their burrows allow air and water
to enter soils easily.*

As ecologists study ecosystems, they often turn to the science of meteorology for information. Does the annual rainfall come mostly in one season, or is it spread evenly over the year? How much does the temperature vary between day and night, and through the year? Finding answers to such questions is important because the climate of an area has a tremendous effect on its plant and animal life.

To learn more about the living parts of an ecosystem, you might visit a small pond. To get there, you will probably have to hike through a field or forest. You may cross a stream that flows into the pond, or another that flows out. Clearly, the pond must be affected by other ecosystems, and the pond must affect them.

A pond ecosystem usually contains all of the nonliving factors mentioned above. The sun provides the energy of life. The climate determines how much rain falls in the area, the length of the growing season for plants, and whether the pond is covered with ice in winter. These factors can have a great effect on the life that the pond supports. The underlying rocks and soils affect the chemistry of the water, which in turn helps determine what kinds of plants and animals live in the water. And the life of the pond affects the nonliving environment: When plants and animals die, their remains settle to the bottom and decay there, adding to the bottom muck and making the pond more shallow.

The living parts of the pond ecosystem (and of any ecosystem) can be divided into three groups:

PRODUCERS are green plants which capture radiant energy from the sun and convert it into food energy. They also take substances such as carbon dioxide, water, oxygen, nitrogen, and sulfur from the environment and convert it into plant material that is used as food by other organisms. In fact, green plants might better be called converters than producers. Regardless, all other life in the pond ecosystem depends on green plants. The same is true of forests, prairies, tundra, and oceans.

At a pond you may see cattails growing along the water's edge, water lilies farther out, and perhaps a carpet of duckweed on the water's surface. But the really important producer plants are invisible. Tiny, drifting plants called *phytoplankton* are usually a greater source of food than the big plants you can see. Sometimes the phytoplankton are so abundant that they give a pond or lake a green color.

CONSUMERS are animals that depend on green plants for food. Some feed directly on the plants while others eat animals that have eaten plants. The plant-feeders include tiny animals called *zooplankton*, which eat phytoplankton, and larger organisms, such as pollywogs, insects, and snails, which eat larger plants. The plant-eaters, or *herbivores*, get their energy directly from the green plants. The other consumers are either *carnivores* (which usually eat herbivores) or *omnivores* (which eat both plants and animals). The carnivores in a pond ecosystem include fish, herons, and insects such as giant water beetles. Raccoons and people are omnivores.

These mushrooms are the visible part of a fungus plant, a decomposer living on energy from a dead tree.

DECOMPOSERS are the third major group of organisms. They use dead plant and animal material as food. The decomposers break down this material, getting the energy they need to live and releasing minerals and other nutrients back into the environment. Most decomposers are simple plants such as bacteria and fungi. These microscopic organisms can be found everywhere in a pond, but are especially abundant at the bottom, where the dead parts of plants and animals settle. On land, decomposers are most abundant at or near the surface of the soil.

Decomposers are the janitors of nature. Without them, everything that died would just lie wherever it fell. Raw materials such as carbon, phosphorus, and nitrogen would be tied up in dead remains and would be unavailable for new life. The decomposers release these vital materials into the soil, water, or air and enable them to be used again and again.

A visit to a pond offers another important lesson about ecology: You can't even see the phytoplankton producers and the bacteria and fungi decomposers. In a pond and in other ecosystems, some of the most important organisms and processes are hidden from our eyes.

Keep in mind the three major groups of living things in ecosystems—producers, consumers, and decomposers. No matter what ecosystem you visit, you'll find signs of all three. Even in a city lot, you can find weeds (producers) fed upon by insects (consumers), while the bacteria and fungi (decomposers) are invisibly at work among the rubbish and dead leaves on the ground.

You may notice that certain kinds of organisms have a specific task in an ecosystem. Ecologists call this task a *niche*. No two kinds (species) of plant or animal in a community can have the exact same niche for long. When they do, they compete with one another and one species eventually dies out. The bison used to be the main grazing animal of the North American plains. That was its niche. Now that niche is filled in some areas by cattle and in others by sheep.

There are several kinds of grazing mammals on the plains of Africa. At first you might think that they all had the same niche, but that isn't so. Giraffes feed on trees, rhinoceroses on brush, and wildebeests on grass. Even

Each grazing animal in Africa has a different task or niche.

*The praying mantis is a predator of insects
that live in fields and meadows.*

among the animals that eat grass, each species has a different niche. Red oats grass is the major food of three grazing species—wildebeests, topis, and zebras. But the wildebeests feed mostly on the short, fresh leaves of this grass. Zebras eat the grass when it is older, but avoid it when the leaves are dry. Topis eat the dry leaves. Each species has a different niche and, in this way, each can survive in the same ecosystem.

The living things in an ecosystem affect each other in many ways. The consumers that kill other animals for food are called *predators*. The word predator usually brings to mind pictures of lions and wolves, but such creatures as robins, frogs, and humans are also predators. Some predators, carnivores such as lions, depend entirely on animals they kill, while many others, such as foxes and humans, eat plant food too.

Some people think of predators as "bad," though humans themselves are the greatest predators the world has known. Sometimes individual predators do prey upon farm animals, and these individuals have to be controlled. Too often, however, people try to wipe out entire populations of predators, with the mistaken idea that they are doing good.

People usually believe that predators have an easy time of it, killing defenseless prey. But studies of predators and their prey show that this isn't so. After observing tigers in Africa, Dr. George Schaller wrote: "The tiger's seemingly unbeatable array of weapons—its acute senses, great speed (but over short distances only), strength and size, and formidable claws and teeth—have given many naturalists the impression that the tiger can kill at will. . . . My experience shows quite the contrary—the tiger has to work quite hard for its meals. . . . I estimate that, for every wild prey killed, the tiger makes twenty to thirty unsuccessful attempts."

Another biologist made the same observation about wolves. After studying North American wolves for twelve years, Dr. L. David Mech concluded that these predators often fail to kill prey that they find. Also, wolves tend to kill animals that are either young, old, sick, weak, injured or diseased. Dr. Mech wrote: "As is true with most predators, the wolf is an opportunist. . . . The predator takes whatever it can catch. If the wolf could capture prime, healthy prey, it certainly would. But most of the time it cannot. It happens that all the prey species of the wolf are well equipped with superb detection, defense, and escape systems. As long as these systems are in good working order, a prey animal is usually safe from wolf attack."

Predators are usually bigger and fewer in number than the animals they prey upon. The reverse is true of *parasites*. These organisms live on or in other living things—their hosts, often spending an entire lifetime with them. In parasitism the parasite gets food and sometimes shelter, while the host gains nothing and may even suffer in some way from the relationship.

Very few living things are free of parasites, which are usually smaller and more numerous than their hosts. Indeed, many parasites have parasites of their own. Jonathan Swift exaggerated only a little when he wrote:

So, naturalists observe, a flea
Hath smaller fleas that on him prey;
And these have smaller still to bite 'em,
And so proceed *ad infinitum*.

Some biologists believe that most of the individual organisms now living are parasites, since there are so many parasitic fungi, bacteria, flatworms, insects, ticks, and mites. Parasites are an important part of all communities and, like predators, often affect the numbers of other organisms in a community. Man has tried to use this ecological knowledge by deliberately bringing parasites or predators into an area where they might control the numbers of some pest. Sometimes this works well; often it does not.

The sea lamprey is a parasite of salmon and other large fish.

In the 1870s, sugar-cane planters in Jamaica were losing about a fifth of their crops to rats, and a planter brought mongooses from India in hopes that they would prey on the rats. Within a few years the number of rats had dropped dramatically. The rats became harder to find. Then the mongooses began eating native mammals, ground-nesting birds, snakes, lizards, land crabs, and anything else they could find. They even took to eating sugar cane. Some of the creatures they wiped out had been useful controls on insect numbers, and the insect damage to sugar cane increased. The mongooses themselves became pests in need of control.

In another instance, house sparrows were brought to the United States from England in hopes that they would help control elm spanworms in New York City's Central Park. The birds did not control the insects and have spread across most of the nation, crowding out bluebirds and other native birds with which they compete for food and nesting sites.

People do learn from their mistakes, and experiences with mongooses, house sparrows, and other introduced organisms led to the passage of strict laws controlling the importation of plants and animals to the United States. The idea of using parasites and predators to control pests has not been abandoned; it is just done with much greater care and advance study. This method of limiting the numbers of pests is called *biological control,* and there is hope that it will someday eliminate the need for many of the insect poisons used today.

The close association between parasite and host is an example of *symbiosis,* which means "living together."

There are a number of other examples of symbiosis in nature. In some relationships, one organism benefits and the other is not affected at all. This is called *commensalism*. Fish called remoras attach themselves to sharks. They get a free ride and eat fragments of the sharks' food. There are many other commensal relationships in the sea. Practically every worm burrow, shellfish, and sponge contains animals that depend on the host for shelter or food scraps. A biologist found 13,500 animals living within the pores of a large sponge collected off the Florida Keys. The animals were mostly small shrimps, but the total included nineteen species, among them a small fish.

In some symbiotic relationships, both organisms benefit. The most common and widespread example of this *mutualism* is a team of plants called the lichen. You can find lichens clinging to rocks and tree trunks almost anywhere. Part of the lichen is a fungus. Within it are colonies of green algae cells. The fungus provides support and traps water which is used by the algae. The algae make food which is consumed by the fungus. Thus both kinds of plant benefit.

The organisms that make up a lichen couldn't survive long apart. In other cases of mutualism, the two organisms may be together only part of the time. Birds called egrets often perch on the backs of African mammals such as rhinoceroses. The birds feed on lice and ticks in the mammal's skin. This benefits both organisms. Also, the rhinoceros may be warned of danger when an egret flies in fright from its back. But neither species is so dependent on the other that it can't survive by itself.

You can probably observe another example of mutualism

Marineland of Florida

Remoras ride on sharks (left) *but do not harm them in this commensal relationship. A lichen on a rock* (above) *and birds eating insect pests from an impala* (right) *are examples of mutualism.*

on a rose bush or other garden plant. There you may find tiny insects called aphids, which get their food by sucking juices from plants. Watch to see if there are any ants near the aphids. Some species of ants have a mutualistic relationship with aphids. The ants protect the aphids and sometimes carry them to good feeding places. You may see an ant stroke an aphid with its antennae. This prompts the aphid to release a drop of sweet liquid from its abdomen. The ant drinks the liquid.

Dozens of other mutualistic relationships have been observed, both on land and in the sea. Probably more will be discovered. Many biologists have devoted their lives to the study of symbiosis, predation, or other relationships between organisms. The rest of this book could easily be filled with details about these fascinating relationships. But the science of ecology is concerned with more than living communities of plants and animals. To really understand the workings of ecosystems, ecologists must learn more about the nonliving environment and how it affects all living things, including humans.

3

Patterns of Life on the Earth

Bison . . . kangaroos . . . zebras. These mammals are strikingly different in many ways, yet they fill similar niches in nature. And their environments are amazingly similar. The grassy prairies of North America are like the grasslands in Africa, Asia, and Australia. The plant life in one grassland resembles that in another.

These facts are useful to ecologists as they try to understand the web of nature. Discoveries they make about a grassland in Montana may also apply to the same kind of ecosystem in Africa. This way of studying nature is called the *biome* approach. A biome is a major land ecosystem, a large land area that has a distinct kind of plant life. It may include ecosystems of many kinds, but the whole area is distinguished by a particular kind of plant life such as

In a study of the grassland biome, an ecologist clips the "standing crop" of plants to estimate the amount of food available to insects, rabbits and other grassland animals.

grassland, rain forest, or whatever characterizes the biome.

Recently a team of about a hundred scientists began working together on studies at the Pawnee National Grasslands in northeastern Colorado. Included in the team were entomologists, wildlife biologists, zoologists, ornithologists, aquatic biologists, range scientists, ecologists, biomathematicians, microbiologists, climatologists, hydrologists, and agronomists. When their work is completed, some of the findings may apply only to their study area, but other discoveries may be true of the grassland biome anywhere on earth.

The location of biomes over the earth is determined mostly by climate, especially by rainfall and temperature. And climate itself is determined by many factors including latitude (distance from the equator), ocean currents, topography, and the prevailing winds. The world's main biomes are shown in the map on page 33.

Even though the map shows clear boundaries between

biomes, the biomes themselves don't begin and end sharply. They blend together at their borders, sometimes over a span of many miles. This zone between two biomes or between two ecosystems is called an *ecotone*. There are ecotones all around us—the shore of a pond, the bank of a stream, the edge between a forest and a meadow. Usually

Ecotones between three ecosystems—stream, meadow, forest

there is a great variety of life in ecotones because animals living there have the best of two worlds, getting food, shelter, and other necessities from two different ecosystems.

Within the boundaries of biomes you may find areas with plant life quite different from that of the whole biome. Often this is an effect of topography. The climate at the top of a mountain ridge is cooler than that of the surrounding land, so plants usually found in a more northern biome may grow on the ridge.

Even though the word "biome" may be new to you, you often think in terms of these major ecosystems. The words "desert" or "prairie" bring to mind pictures of these areas, with their characteristic plants and animals. The next several pages describe some of the major biomes of the world.

TUNDRA means "marshy plain" in Russian. It is a vast treeless land, dotted with lakes, ponds, and bogs. It totals about five million acres and encircles the top of the world, stretching southward from the north polar seas and ending where it meets the northern evergreen forests. Even though the tundra seems like a water-rich land, especially during its brief summer, it is a sort of arctic desert. The annual precipitation is low and the water is frozen and not available to living things during the nine- to ten-month winter.

Only the top layer of soil thaws in the summer. Beneath that, sometimes reaching many feet below the surface of

BIOMES OF THE WORLD

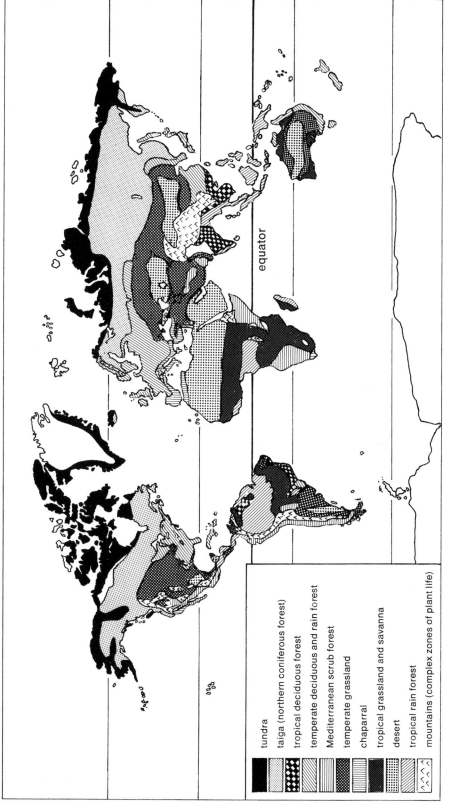

equator

tundra
taiga (northern coniferous forest)
tropical deciduous forest
temperate deciduous and rain forest
Mediterranean scrub forest
temperate grassland
chaparral
tropical grassland and savanna
desert
tropical rain forest
mountains (complex zones of plant life)

Based on biome map in Eugene P. Odum, *Fundamentals of Ecology*, 2d edn. (Philadelphia, W. B. Saunders Co., 1959).

the ground, is permanently frozen ground, called *perma-frost*. A thick mat of grasses, sedges, mosses, lichens, dwarf willow, and birch trees covers the soil. The tundra plants cram all their growing and flowering into the brief summer period. At the same time, hordes of ducks, geese, and shore-birds raise their young there, then fly south as the long, dark arctic winter approaches.

Some birds and mammals live year-round in the arctic tundra. They include polar bears, musk oxen, arctic hares, arctic foxes, lemmings, ptarmigan, and snowy owls. Car-ibou and reindeer travel south to the shelter of forests in

Can man use the resources of the tundra without doing great damage to this fragile land?

wintertime. (The caribou of North America occupy the same niche as the reindeer of northern Europe and Siberia.)

At many places on the earth, even at the equator, if you climb to the top of a mountain you will find an environment that seems like the arctic tundra, only drier. This is *alpine tundra,* found above the timberline on high mountains. The climate on a mountaintop is much like that of the Arctic, although there is no permafrost and the growing season is usually longer. Alpine tundra is often a carpet of low, flowering plants, but the colder mountaintops bear

mostly lichens and mosses, much like the biome near the top of the world.

Humans have barely affected the arctic tundra, though Eskimos, Indians, and Lapps have been a part of this biome for thousands of years. Now the growing human population and its demand for resources threaten great change. The discovery of oil in northern Alaska raised questions about how the oil industry could operate without harming tundra ecosystems. Ecologists had no quick answers because so little is known about the tundra. They warned, however, that a huge oil spill might be a long-lasting disaster. Because of permafrost, oil might just lie on top of the land and not drain away. Because of the cold temperatures, wastes of all kinds decay slowly in the Arctic. If people don't treat the tundra with great care, the wounds could be massive and would take many years to heal.

TAIGA, or northern coniferous forest, is made up almost completely of spruce and fir trees. It lies south of the tundra and covers a broad zone across North America, Europe, and Asia. Taiga forests reach southward along mountain ranges such as the Rockies and Appalachians.

Since taiga lies closer to the equator than tundra, it receives more energy from the sun. Snowfall is greater and the snow insulates the soil, preventing permafrost in most areas. The needlelike leaves of the evergreen trees have a

Moose are the large herbivores of the taiga.

waxy coating that protects them from the cold and reduces the loss of water to the air. Little sunlight slips through the evergreens to the forest floor, so few plants grow there.

Even though most of the taiga is made up of evergreens, there are other trees, such as birches, willows, and aspens, which are favored foods of moose and beavers. The evergreens are the main habitat of red squirrels, martens, and such seed-eating birds as siskins and crossbills. Taiga winters are long and cold, but the insulating snow cover, and the food and shelter of trees make it possible for a greater variety of animals to survive there than in the tundra to the north.

The climate of the taiga has kept people from living there in great numbers. So far, people have used taiga mostly as a source of lumber and paper pulp. Explorers are searching for fuel and mineral treasures under the taiga. The demand for all of these resources will increase with population growth.

TEMPERATE DECIDUOUS FOREST covers most of the eastern United States, Great Britain, eastern Asia, and almost all of central Europe. The growing season is warm and long, and there are forty inches or more of rainfall spread evenly through the year. A greater variety of plants and animals lives in this biome than in the taiga and tundra.

Temperate deciduous forest in Virginia

Most of the trees are deciduous, dropping their leaves in the autumn. They include oak, maple, beech, elm, birch, and ash. Enough of the sun's energy gets through the upper leafy crowns, the *canopy*, of tall trees to support another layer of trees, the understory, and abundant shrubs, ferns, and wildflowers. Many of the wildflowers grow and bloom in the springtime, before the trees overhead leaf out and reduce the sunlight reaching the ground.

Since there are a great variety and abundance of plant producers, there are also many animal consumers. Insects live in all layers of the forest, and different species of insect-eating birds feed in different layers or parts of the forest. Ovenbirds seek food on the forest floor; vireos hunt high in the canopy; woodpeckers probe under tree bark. The forests also are homes for reptiles, amphibians, and such mammals as deer, foxes, squirrels, and bats.

The climate of the temperate deciduous forest appeals to humans, and man has left his mark on this biome. Vast areas have been cleared for farming and for the building of homes, highways, and industries. Chicago, Boston, Philadelphia, and New York City stand where deciduous forests once grew.

The remaining forest has been changed in many ways, probably including some of which we are not even aware. Air pollution kills or damages some tree species. An Asian fungus, introduced accidentally by man, wiped out the American chestnut, which was an important part of the deciduous forest in eastern North America. People also eliminated wolves and mountain lions from the deciduous forests. With these big carnivores gone, their prey, especially deer, sometimes become so plentiful that they deplete their own food supply and die of starvation.

Some forest animals have benefited from the changes made by people. Deer, woodchucks, cottontail rabbits, and several species of bird thrive in an environment that is a mixture of forest and more open land. The American robin, which used to live mostly near the edge of forest clearings, has apparently increased greatly in numbers and extended its range because of man-made changes in the deciduous forest biome.

TROPICAL RAIN FOREST is incredibly rich with plant and animal life. It covers vast low-lying areas near the equator, in the Amazon Basin, Central America, central and western Africa, and the Malay–New Guinea region. Rain falls almost every day, with at least eighty inches during the year. There is plenty of sun energy, and little change in temperature from day to night or month to month.

This warm, wet climate produces a great abundance and variety of plants, including thousands of species of tall evergreen trees. The trees support many climbing vines, and a variety of *epiphytes,* which cling to the trees but which, unlike vines, have no connection with the ground. (The trees and epiphytes have a commensal relationship.) Epiphytes catch rainwater in special roots that dangle in the air, or in the hollows of specially shaped leaves.

*Life is espe-
cially abun-
dant and
varied in the
canopy of the
tropical rain
forest.*

Tropical epiphytes include orchids, peppers, ferns, brome-
liads (relatives of pineapples), and even cacti.

The ever-warm, ever-moist conditions of the tropics are
ideal for decomposers, and leaves that fall to the forest floor
decay very quickly. In fact, you may travel on bare soil
while hiking through the rain forest. The interior of a rain
forest is usually open and uncluttered, though dark. It is

not the tangled jungle that many people picture. Only along roads, rivers, and on formerly cleared land—the places people see most often—does enough sunlight reach the ground to produce a thick "jungle" of plants.

Life in most forest biomes is especially abundant on the forest floor; in the rain forest the tree canopy is the liveliest place. Besides insects and birds that you expect to see high in the treetops, there are many kinds of tree-dwelling mammals such as monkeys, fruit bats, sloths, and lemurs. There are also tree frogs, tree snakes, and tree lizards. In addition to the many thousands of insect species, there are other invertebrates (animals without backbones), such as centipedes, millipedes, scorpions, snails, worms, and spiders, lurking among the leaves and under loose bark. One entomologist found twenty thousand different kinds of insects in six square miles of Panamanian rain forest; in contrast, there are only a few hundred insect species in all of France.

Scientists are still mostly in the "what is it?" stage in the tropical rain forest, trying to identify the life that exists there. Since the complex rain forest ecosystems are so poorly understood, it is not surprising that changes made there by man sometimes have had disastrous results. When trees are felled and the land is cleared for farming, the soil quickly loses its fertility. In rain forests nearly all of the minerals are tied up in living plants and animals. At any one time the amount of minerals in the soil is very small. When trees are cleared from the land, rainwater soon carries the vital minerals deeper into the soil, beyond the roots of man's crops.

Although people are successfully raising coffee, rubber, sugar cane, cocoa, and other crops where rain forests once grew, many other farming efforts have ended with ruined soil that had to be abandoned. If rain forest is destroyed over a large area, it doesn't grow back but is replaced by a junglelike growth or grassland dotted with trees (sa-

vanna). The present rapid growth of human population in tropical countries means that people will be clearing more and more rain forest, long before they understand how this complex biome "works."

GRASSLAND occurs where the annual rainfall is between ten and thirty inches. This biome covers a third of the United States and large areas of all continents. In North America the eastern grasslands are called prairies, the western ones are called plains. Grasslands are called pampas in South America, steppes in the Soviet Union, veld in South Africa. In the grasslands of North America, the plants tend to be shorter as you travel from east to west. In fact, the grasslands are often called (from east to west): tall grass prairie, mixed prairie, and short grass plains. The amount of rainfall determines what species of plant grow in the grasslands, and the annual precipitation decreases from east to west across the middle of the United States.

Natural grasslands support many large grazing mammals, such as bison, antelopes, and kangaroos. Since there are few hiding places on the prairie, some mammals are swift runners while others, including ground squirrels and gophers, escape to burrows. Grasshoppers and other plant-eating insects are plentiful, and so are birds that feed on insects, mice, or other herbivores.

At one time, about 40 per cent of the land on earth was covered with natural grassland. Now most of it is farmland

The National Bison Range in Montana is an example of the grassland

or wasteland. The grassland biome has probably been used
—and abused—more than any other. The moister grasslands are excellent for raising corn and wheat; the drier
ones support cattle and sheep. Many thousands of acres
have been overgrazed and so eroded that the soils no longer
support much life; these grasslands have become man-
made deserts.

DESERTS cover about 14 per cent of the earth's
land surface and occur on all continents. Only ten inches
of rain or less falls each year, and much of this evaporates
quickly because of the high temperatures, frequent strong
winds, and bright, cloudless days. Desert climates do vary,
however. The more northern deserts are often bitter cold in
winter, with some snowfall. The Sahara Desert of northern

biome that is found on all continents.

Africa is the hottest and biggest; the Gobi of Mongolia is the coldest.

People usually picture barren sand dunes when they think of deserts, but you can travel a hundred miles through North American deserts without seeing a single dune. Most desert is a bush-covered land, with much bare ground between the bushes. In some species, the spacing between plants seems to be caused by poisonous substances given off by the plant roots or leaves. These poisons kill seedlings that may start to grow near a bush. This tends to keep plants spaced apart, and reduces competition for water between individual plants.

As in all biomes, the desert is home for plants and animals that are specially adapted for life in that environment. Many desert plants have small leaves or no leaves; this helps them conserve water. Cactus plants store water

and swell up during the rainy season, then shrink as the dry months pass and most of the water is used. Some plants avoid the problem of water supply entirely. During the brief rainy season they sprout, grow, and flower. For a few days the desert is a colorful carpet of flowers. Then the plants die. Their seeds have tough coats which protect them until the next rainfall.

Like the plants, desert animals are either drought-resisters or drought-evaders. Most desert mammals drink little or no water. They get the water they need from their food, and stay in burrows or in shade during the heat of the day. Some even go into a deep sleep, called *estivation,* during the driest months of the year.

Compared to the deciduous forests and grasslands, deserts have not been changed much by man. But people are turning to deserts more and more for farmland and home sites. Desert soils are often fertile and produce abundant crops if irrigation water is brought to them. To get this water, people sometimes tap supplies that have been stored for centuries deep beneath the desert floor. Once this "mined" water is gone, the farms have to be abandoned unless another source is found. Sometimes irrigation water causes a buildup of salts in the soil that prevents crops from growing. The ruins of old settlements and irrigation systems in deserts should warn us that these dry lands may not continue to bloom unless we learn more about them and make changes with great care.

Shrubs and saguaro cacti compete for water in this Arizona desert.

OTHER BIOMES include the tropical deciduous forest, the savanna, and the Mediterranean scrub forest. The last kind occurs where there are mild, wet winters and long, dry summers. In North America, this type of biome is called chaparral and occurs along the coasts of

southern California and northern Mexico. Most of the trees and shrubs have hard, thick evergreen leaves. When the plants dry out in the summer, fires may sweep through the chaparral with incredible speed, bringing death and de-

Chaparral in the Los Padres National Forest in California

struction to the people who choose to live there. But fire has always been a normal part of the chaparral biome; it helps the sprouting of some kinds of seeds, and the other plant life recovers quickly.

The distribution of biomes, determined mostly by climate, applies only to the pattern of life on land. That leaves the other 70 per cent of the world—the oceans—as well as freshwater streams, ponds, and lakes. Climate has some effect on these ecosystems, but the effect is not as great as on land. The water environments of the world are not divided into biomes, but ecologists classify them in other ways, for example, fresh water and salt water. Of course, nature often doesn't fit easily into the classification systems used by man. Fresh and salt water mix where rivers enter oceans. Such places are called *estuaries,* but it is difficult to tell exactly where an estuary ends and the ocean begins.

OCEANS are easily the biggest and least under-stood of all ecosystems on earth. The nonliving parts of the ocean environment include waves, tides, currents, temperatures, pressures, and the amounts of light and salts. Although there are some large sea plants, such as kelp, the most important producers by far are the tiny, drifting plants called phytoplankton, especially diatoms and dino-flagellates.

Living things can be found anywhere in the ocean, even miles below the surface, but vast stretches of the sea have little life. The phytoplankton can manufacture food only

"Yeah, it's a big ocean
—but those were big
lakes, too."
Copyright 1970 by
Herblock in The
Washington Post

where sunlight reaches, so most of these tiny plants don't live below two hundred feet. The average depth of the ocean is about 13,000 feet. This means that no food at all is produced in most of the ocean's waters. Animals living in the depths depend on dead plant and animal material that "rains" down from above.

The sea is rich in minerals. Rivers constantly carry them from the land and bacteria release them from dead material on the ocean floor. The minerals would stay on the bottom, however, if it weren't for currents that carry them to the surface zone of light in some areas. In these areas of upwelling currents, the waters are rich with phytoplankton which are fed upon by zooplankton, which in turn become food for large animals such as fish, whales, and sea birds. Most seafood is caught in areas of upwelling currents and

along the coasts of continents where sunlight reaches the bottom and minerals are plentiful. In most of the open sea, there isn't much food produced because of the lack of needed minerals.

Since the ocean environment is so different from that on land, life there is also very different. It begins with the smallest known plants and ends with the largest animals, the whales. There are no ocean insects; the crustaceans (such as shrimps and crabs) are the "insects of the sea" since they occupy many niches in the sea comparable to niches filled by insects on land. There are no starfish or other echinoderms on land. Forty-eight thousand species of echinoderms live in the oceans. The most varied and abundant life is found in and around coral reefs, which occur near shore or in other shallow waters of warm seas. They are like oases in an underwater desert.

Ecologists know most about the *littoral* zone of the ocean —that fascinating strip between high and low tides. This is a demanding environment; the plants and animals there have to survive in a place where twice a day they are submerged in salt water, then exposed to the air. Barnacles, limpets, and chitons cling to rocks and close up tightly to survive the times they are not under water. Other creatures burrow in the sand. The life patterns of some animals are finely tuned to the patterns of the nonliving environment in the littoral zone. On the west coast of the United States, for example, a small fish called the grunion spawns on sandy shores only during the highest tides, between nine and twelve o'clock on the night of a full moon.

Beyond the littoral zone, and especially beyond the continental shelf, our knowledge of the ocean ecosystem is slight. The oceans are a frontier which we have hardly begun to explore. So far, one of our most important discoveries about the oceans has been that they are not as rich with food as people once thought. Present fish catches may be doubled or tripled, but we can't count on what used to be called "the limitless riches of the sea" to solve the food needs of a rapidly growing population.

ESTUARIES are sometimes called bays, tidal marshes, or sounds. They are the places where fresh water from a river meets the salt water of the ocean. The saltiness of an estuary varies; there is usually less fresh water flowing into the estuary in the summer. The mixing of the lighter fresh water with the heavier salt water tends to keep the minerals and other nutrients circulating in the estuary, instead of being immediately swept out to sea. Because of this "nutrient trap," estuaries are rich with food, including blue crabs, lobsters, oysters, scallops, and many kinds of fish. One ecologist estimated that estuaries produce twenty times as much food as an equal area of open sea.

Estuaries have been called the "cradles of the sea." Ocean fish such as mullet, menhaden, striped bass, and shad lay their eggs in estuaries and the young spend part of their lives there. The great value of estuaries as nurseries for sea life and as sources of food is unknown or ignored by many people. As a result, estuaries are being rapidly de-

Estuaries are ecotones between fresh and salt water,
and are rich with plant and animal life. They are
rapidly being altered and destroyed by humans.

stroyed—filled in, poisoned, polluted. There is no better example of man's ignorance of the web of nature on which his survival depends.

LAKES AND PONDS share some characteristics with oceans. Big lakes have depths where sunlight never reaches. The bigger and deeper the lake, the more important are the phytoplankton, rather than other plants, as food producers in the ecosystem.

One big difference between lakes and oceans, besides the amount of salts dissolved in the water, is that the oceans are so vast that the land environment has little effect on them. Lakes and ponds can be greatly affected by changes that occur in the surrounding land from which their waters drain (the *watershed*). Although these standing bodies of water often have outlet streams, they are mostly closed ecosystems. Most of the material that enters a lake or pond stays there. The basin of a lake or pond gradually fills up, first becoming a marsh and eventually dry land (see pages 104–05).

Life is most abundant in the lake and pond waters where sunlight reaches the bottom and rooted plants provide food and hiding places. Aquatic insects, crustaceans, and fish make up the bulk of the animal life. The edges (ecotones) of ponds and lakes are especially good places to see wildlife. Frogs, turtles, and snakes often come ashore or near it in their quest for foods; land animals such as raccoons and deer also feed along the edges.

Compared with ecosystems in the tundra or ocean, ponds

and small lakes are handy and easy to study. Some of the most important discoveries about ecosystems, how they "work," and how they change with time have been revealed in studies of ponds. Of course, the handiness of lakes and ponds also makes it easy for people to change them by draining, filling, dumping wastes, overfishing, or putting new kinds of living things in the water.

RIVERS AND STREAMS make up a very small part of the total surface of the earth but of all the ecosystems they are perhaps the most intensely used by people. Throughout the history of man they have been used for water, power, food, recreation, transportation, and waste disposal. Today the sickest rivers are in the nations considered to be the richest and most advanced. Unlike lakes and ponds, rivers and streams are open ecosystems. Minerals and other nutrients enter them from watersheds and are carried steadily downstream. They don't accumulate as they would in the basin of a lake.

As you walk along a stream, you may see fast-flowing rapids and quiet pools. Even though these two environments are only a few feet apart, the plant-animal communities may be quite different. The fast current scours the stream bottom in the rapids. When the water slows in a pool, dead leaves and particles of soil and rock settle to the bottom. Most of the decomposers in a stream live in pools or in other areas of slow-moving water.

Animals such as trout move freely from rapids to pools and back. Other creatures, however, spend all of their lives

LIFE IN A FAST-FLOWING STREAM

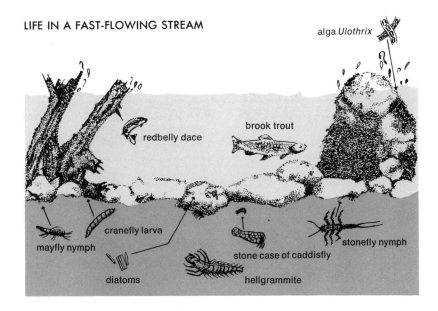

alga *Ulothrix*

brook trout

redbelly dace

cranefly larva

mayfly nymph

stonefly nymph

stone case of caddisfly

diatoms

hellgrammite

LIFE IN A SLOW-FLOWING STREAM

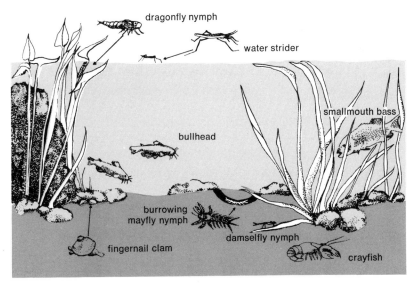

dragonfly nymph

water strider

smallmouth bass

bullhead

burrowing
mayfly nymph

damselfly nymph

fingernail clam

crayfish

After Fig. 10–5 (p. 199) "Life in a fast stream compared to that in a slow stream," in *Ecology and Field Biology,* by Robert L. Smith, illustrated by Ned Smith (Harper & Row, 1966)

A slow-flowing river may form a meandering pattern on the land.

in one stream environment. The young of some insects cling to rocks and are able to dart along the bottom against the swift current. If you put them in a quiet pool or in a home aquarium, they die because there is no current to aid their breathing and to bring them food.

As a river or stream nears an ocean or lake, it flows slowly and drops more and more fine particles of soil (*silt*) on its bottom. Dead plant material builds up on the bottom, attracting many more decomposers and bottom-dwelling fish. Slow-flowing rivers resemble ponds, with turtles sun-ning on logs and cattails and pickerelweeds growing along the shore. Plankton populations are never great in rivers and streams, but they do add to the food production of sluggish streams.

Few streams exist that haven't been affected by humans through pollution by silt, sewage, or industrial wastes. Given a chance, a stream can rid itself of many pollutants. The decomposers clean them up just as they do a dead leaf or the body of a fish. But nowadays the load of wastes in streams is sometimes so great that the decomposers can-not cope with it. Even if no more pollutants were added, it would take years for many rivers to cleanse themselves.

When ecologists study biomes and ecosystems, they try to understand nature as it existed before humans made great changes. This is increasingly difficult because all of the web of nature has been affected by man and some eco-systems have been greatly modified. Man's effects on nature can't be ignored. This doesn't mean that ecologists will stop investigating nature in those wild areas that have been little touched by man. It does mean, however, that ecol-ogists will devote more effort to understanding "man-made" ecosystems. Take, for example, the "big city" or "suburban sprawl" ecosystems. You won't find them listed in any text-book on ecology. Yet these are the ecosystems where many people live and work, and surprisingly little is known about them.

In a "big city" ecosystem, most of the land has been covered with concrete, macadam, steel, stone, wood, brick,

*We have much
to learn about
the big city
ecosystem.*

and glass. The climate of the original ecosystem remains, but even this is affected by man. A city makes its own special climate. Heat from the sun is soaked up by buildings. It is gradually released at night, so the day and night temperatures don't vary as much as those in the countryside. Scientists have recently discovered that cities tend to have more cloudy days, more fog, more rain or snow, and slower winds than the countryside around them.

In city parks and along streets you may find some survivors of the original ecosystem plant and animal life. Some kinds of trees may have died out because of air pollution. Sometimes they are replaced by species from another country, like the ginkgo from China, which can survive better in polluted air. City animals are mostly species that people keep as pets, or that people tolerate (such as pigeons),

In the country, most of the sun's rays are reflected
back into the atmosphere. In cities, sun's rays are reflected
to buildings, which absorb heat. City air warms
more quickly and cools more slowly than country air.

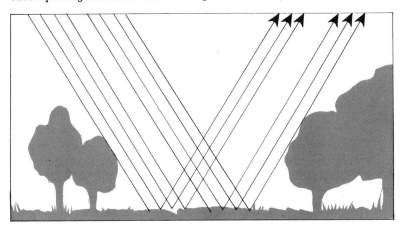

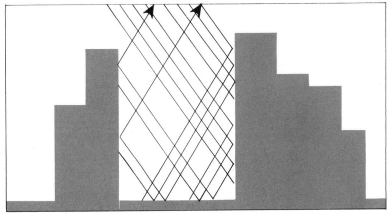

or that survive despite efforts to get rid of them. Rats and cockroaches can be found in nearly every city in the world; other kinds of animals vary from city to city but they often fill the same niches. The house finch of Denver and other Western cities has a way of life similar to the house sparrow of Eastern cities.

Surprisingly little is known about the common large mammals—humans—and about how they are affected by the environment they have created. Is noise an important cause of stress in humans? What are the effects of different air pollutants on human health? These questions deal with an organism and its relations to its environment. Clearly, the science of ecology doesn't stop at the city line.

In city lots you may find some survivors of the living things that were part of the area's original ecosystem.

4

The Flow of Energy

Ninety-three million miles from earth is a star we call the sun. This star gives off fantastic amounts of radiant energy, but only a fraction reaches the earth and its atmosphere. Much of that is reflected from clouds back into space. Of all the radiant energy reaching the atmosphere, only about two fifths gets to the earth's surface. Some of this is reflected away and most of the rest is absorbed and warms the surface of the earth. About one tenth of 1 per cent is captured by green plants. It is this energy that supports all of the life on earth. You might think of it as the fuel that drives the engine of the earth ecosystem. The sun provides the energy for a bird's song, a deer's leap, and for you to hold this book and read these words.

In the cells of green plants the sun's energy, along with

Energy from the sun drives the earth ecosystem,
and green plants convert the solar energy
to food energy used by plants and animals.

water and carbon dioxide, is converted to simple sugars. This vital process is called *photosynthesis,* which means "putting together with light." During photosynthesis radiant energy is converted into chemical energy. The chemical energy can be used by the green plants themselves and by the consumers and decomposers that depend on them.

Unlike minerals and other nutrients, energy is not recycled in nature. Life can exist on earth only as long as it receives its fuel from the sun. Most of the energy that comes to the earth is eventually lost to the atmosphere as heat. This happens whenever energy is changed in form or transferred from one organism to another. You are probably most aware of this heat loss when you run fast or work hard. The food energy stored in your body (*potential energy*) is being changed to energy of motion (*kinetic energy*). In the process a lot of the potential energy is given off in the form of heat. This makes you feel hot.

Since energy is lost whenever it is changed in form or transferred, organisms pass on less energy than they receive. When a rabbit eats a green plant it receives chemical energy, but the energy it gets is much less than the amount the plant received from the sun. When a coyote, in turn, eats the rabbit, it receives chemical energy from it but gets much less than the rabbit received from the plant. By the time decomposers finish the decay of the coyote, the original energy received by the green plant is almost all gone.

The percentage of available energy passed along probably varies a great deal, but isn't very high. In one laboratory study, an ecologist found it to be 10 per cent. He discovered that tiny crustaceans received only 10 per cent of the total energy produced by the algae plants they ate. Then hydras, the animals that fed on the crustaceans, received 10 per cent of that, or just 1 per cent of the total energy.

Energy takes many different pathways through the living community of an ecosystem. These pathways, which can be called *food chains,* follow the step-by-step flow of energy through a series of organisms. Green plant→rabbit→coyote is one food chain. In the ocean, a chain might be: phytoplankton→zooplankton→small fish→big fish→human. Food chains are an easy way to show how energy is passed from one organism to another, but they don't give an accurate picture of the complexity of nature. For example, decomposers get their energy from every link in the chain, and many organisms besides small fish feed upon plankton in the oceans. A more realistic picture of energy flow is a *food web,* with many food chains interlinked and crisscrossed.

Recently ecologists have been able to study actual food chains by using radioactive tracers. In Tennessee, they put a solution containing a tiny amount of radioactive phosphorus on the leaves and stems of some grass plants. Over the next few weeks the ecologists caught small animals in the grass and used a device to measure the amount of radioactive phosphorus the animals contained. Small crickets and ants were the first to reach a peak of radioactivity. Large plant eaters such as grasshoppers reached a peak later. Spiders and other predators had their peak in radioactivity after about four weeks had passed, as did the snails and beetles living in the surface litter under the grasses.

FOOD CHAIN

A food chain shows the path of energy from one organism to another, but does not illustrate the real complexity of nature.

FOOD WEB

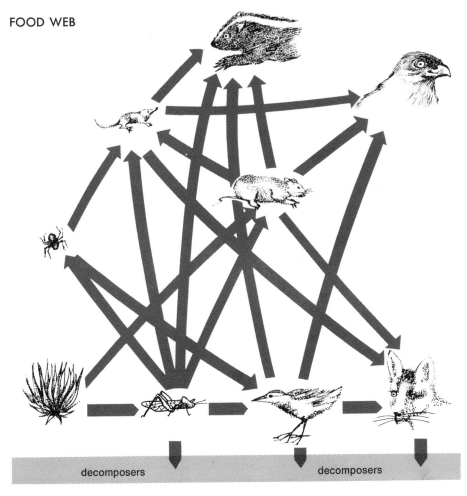

decomposers   decomposers

This food web shows the same organisms that appear in the food chain above. By adding decomposers and other organisms, the diagram begins to suggest the complexity of energy flow in nature.

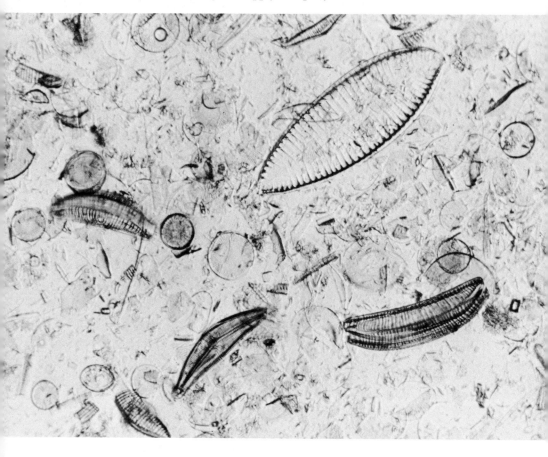

Food chains in water begin with microscopic plants such as diatoms (above). Energy, minerals, and other nutrients are passed from one living thing to another in the chain. Energy is used up by each organism, so it may take thousands of fish and crustaceans to support one seal, and many seals to provide energy for one Eskimo.

Radioactive tracers are an important tool that enables ecologists to follow the flow of materials and energy through the web of nature.

Since energy is lost at each link, a food chain usually has no more than five links and normally has less. The shorter the food chain, the greater the amount of available food energy. This fact is put to use by people all over the world, although they are probably not aware of it. In poor countries, people depend mostly on grains such as rice and wheat for their food. A ten-acre field, properly watered, produces enough rice to feed twenty-four people for a year. If cattle are raised on it, the same field will produce enough beef to feed just one person for a year. By keeping the food chain short (green plant→human), people receive energy that would have been lost as heat from the longer chain of green plant→cattle→human. Each year in the United States it takes more than six hundred billion tons of grain to produce eighty-four billion tons of meat, milk, and eggs.

Scientists are trying to find ways in which people can feed further down on ocean food chains. Most seafood comes from animals that are third, fourth, or even fifth links in food chains. If ways can be found to harvest phytoplankton or zooplankton and make it edible, much more of the food energy in the oceans would be available to people.

The flow of energy in an ecosystem can also be expressed in ecological pyramids. One is a *pyramid of numbers*, which shows the numbers of individual organisms in a food chain. It may take five thousand grass plants to supply energy for five hundred grasshoppers, which supply energy for one bird. These numbers make a pyramid, with the grass plants as the broad base and the single bird on top. But the numbers of organisms are not as important as their total weight, or *biomass*. If, for example, a pyramid of numbers began with oak trees, there would be less of them than of the insects and other herbivores that feed on the trees. Ecologists usually work with two other kinds of ecological pyramids: the *pyramid of biomass* and the *pyramid of energy*.

By actually weighing organisms, ecologists get an idea of the total weight of the living things at each level in a pyramid of numbers. (They prefer to calculate the dry weight, since the percentage of water in different organisms varies a lot.) In a pyramid of biomass, the total weight supported at each level is limited by the rate at which energy is stored by the organisms in the level below. This pyramid shows the biomass at a particular time, or during a certain period. It does not show the total amount of food produced over a long span of time, such as a year.

Because of this, a pyramid of biomass may be upside down, just as is a pyramid of numbers that begins with a few oak trees. When ecologists measured the biomass of plankton in a part of the English Channel, they found a greater weight of zooplankton than phytoplankton. Over a year's time, the phytoplankton have a much greater biomass than the zooplankton. But most of them are eaten as soon as they appear. Thus, at certain times, it is possible to weigh the plankton and find a greater weight of animals than of plants.

A pyramid of energy gives the best overall picture of how

ECOLOGICAL PYRAMIDS

PYRAMID OF NUMBERS

in a bluegrass field

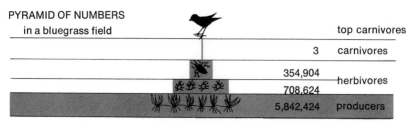

	top carnivores
3	carnivores
354,904	herbivores
708,624	
5,842,424	producers

A pyramid of numbers shows the totals of individual organisms found in an area at a particular time.

PYRAMID OF BIOMASS

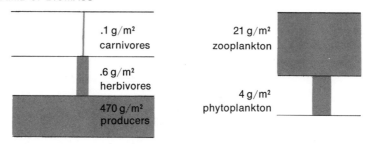

.1 g/m² carnivores

.6 g/m² herbivores

470 g/m² producers

21 g/m² zooplankton

4 g/m² phytoplankton

in an abandoned field in Georgia   in an area of the English Channel

The total weight of organisms in an area at a particular time is shown in a pyramid of biomass. Usually the biomass of producers is much greater than that of consumers, but at certain times there are exceptions (right).

PYRAMID OF ENERGY

in Silver Springs, Florida

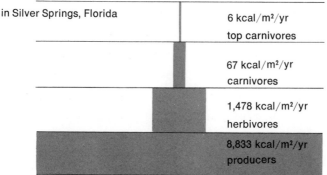

6 kcal/m²/yr
top carnivores

67 kcal/m²/yr
carnivores

1,478 kcal/m²/yr
herbivores

8,833 kcal/m²/yr
producers

This pyramid of energy shows the amounts of energy available to other organisms in a year's time. More energy was produced but was used to meet the needs of the organisms at each level of the pyramid.

energy flows through the living parts of an ecosystem. It takes into account the rate at which food is produced, as well as the total amount. It isn't affected by the size of the organisms, or by how quickly they use the energy that flows to them.

For many years ecologists have tried to measure the production of energy in plants. The first method, still in use, is simply harvesting. In grasslands, for example, ecologists clip all of the plants close to the ground in an area and weigh the material after drying it. This gives them a measurement of the amount of energy stored during the growing season. Similar studies have been made of aquatic and forest plants. This method is not so simple as it may seem. The ecologists have to estimate the amount of energy stored in the roots unless they were harvested too. The harvesting method also fails to account for the plant material eaten by animals.

Better methods for measuring production of energy have become available recently. Using devices such as infrared gas analyzers, ecologists can measure a plant's uptake or output of carbon dioxide or oxygen. From these measurements they are able to determine the rate of photosynthesis and the rate at which the plant is "burning" food energy. From these rates ecologists can estimate the *net productivity* of a plant or plants. Net productivity is the amount of energy stored in a given time. It is the food energy left after the plant has met its own energy needs; it represents the energy that is available for consumers or decomposers.

The basic unit of energy used by ecologists is the *kilocalorie,* the amount of heat needed to raise the temperature

Ecologists using an infrared gas analyzer in alpine tundra (from *Plants and the Ecosystem* by W. D. Billings © 1964 by Wadsworth Publishing Co. Reprinted by permission of the author)

of one liter (1.057 quarts) of water one degree centigrade. The productivity of a plant or of an entire community is often expressed in kilocalories per square meter per year ($kcal/m^2/yr.$). Sometimes units of weight are used, such as grams per square meter per day.

Rates of productivity vary from season to season, day to day, and minute to minute. Green plants stop producing food at night. Tundra plants can produce and store energy only during the short arctic summer. Their productivity during the two- or three-month summer is fairly high, but over the span of an entire year it is very low.

Ecologists have estimated the productivity of different kinds of ecosystems, and have found that the most productive ones are coral reefs, some estuaries, and some areas of sugar cane farms. The least productive ecosystems are the deserts and the oceans. The productivity of an ecosystem doesn't depend as much on the kinds of plants, or land, or water (salt or fresh) as it does on the supply of the sun's energy and raw materials. About 80 per cent of the earth's

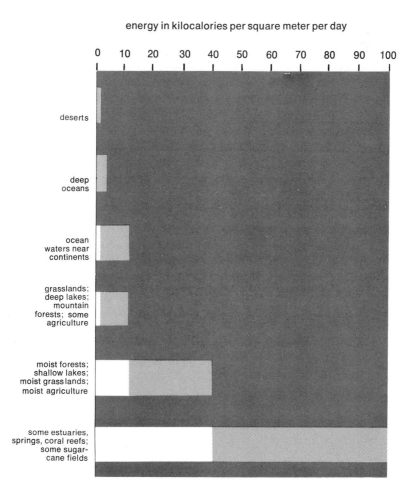

WORLD DISTRIBUTION OF ENERGY PRODUCTION
(area in white and gray shows total energy production;
area in gray shows usual range of energy production)

Adapted from Eugene P. Odum, *Fundamentals of Ecology*, 2d edn.
(Philadelphia, W. B. Saunders Co., 1959).

surface has low productivity, because much of the open sea lacks minerals and deserts lack water.

Discoveries about productivity and energy flow in nature reveal, once again, that the web of nature is more complex than we once thought. At Lake Erken in Sweden, ecologists discovered that the amount of food energy produced by algae was not enough to support the zooplankton of the lake. The zooplankton also fed upon plant and animal debris, and on the bacteria that were living on this material. The food chain was quite different from the ones we usually picture, and investigations into other kinds of ecosystems show that a great deal of energy flows through *detritus* food chains—those based on dead plant and animal material. When an ecologist named Dr. John Teal studied a small spring in Massachusetts, he found that photosynthesis produced only about a quarter of the total energy. The rest came from dead leaves and other once-living material that fell into the spring. This detritus supported most of the life in the spring.

Detritus-based food chains are an important part of many other ecosystems. In a salt marsh, Dr. Teal found that only 10 per cent of the living plant material was eaten by herbivores. The rest of the plants' net productivity flowed through decomposers and animals that fed upon detritus. In forests, great populations of bacteria, ants, earthworms, and other organisms get their energy from the dead material that falls to the forest floor. Ecologists estimate that as much as 90 per cent of the energy in a forest flows through the detritus food chain. That leaves

Most of the energy in forests flows through detritus food chains.

just 10 per cent for animals like vireos, squirrels, and deer —the creatures we usually think of in a forest food chain. The flow of energy through detritus-based food chains is not as noticeable as through other kinds of food chain, but it is obviously a major part of many ecosystems and one which is poorly understood.

Too often people think of energy flow and food chains as something that happens only in forests or far out in the oceans. But humans are at the end of many food chains, and the rapidly growing population is consuming more and more of the total energy produced on earth. If the human population becomes too great, people will have to become herbivores instead of omnivores. There won't be enough energy to waste any on the longer food chains needed to raise meat animals.

People and their wastes are causing a broad pattern of change in the production and flow of energy on the earth. In some ecosystems, the populations of plant-eating animals have been reduced or wiped out, so that more energy flows to the decomposers. Water pollution that causes great growths of algae has the same effect. Both of these changes reduce the amount of energy available to people.

At this point, some readers may be disappointed with the science of ecology. Many people imagine ecologists as scientists who spend most of their time counting deer, watching birds, or netting and measuring fish. Some ecologists do these things some of the time, and there will always be a need for such investigations. But ecologists are turning more and more to computers, infrared gas analyzers, radioactive tracers, and formulas that give figures in kcal/m²/yr. All these tools, and more, are needed if man is ever to understand the complex web of nature.

5

Cycles of Life

Living things get their energy from the sun, but they are made up of elements that come from the earth, water, and air. Plants and animals need at least thirty to forty chemical elements for their growth and development. The amounts that they need vary. Ninety-three per cent of the human body, by weight, is made up of just three elements—oxygen, carbon, and hydrogen. But people also need phosphorus, calcium, nitrogen, iron, and other elements.

There are limited amounts of these elements on earth. No new supply comes from the sun or anywhere else. So, unlike energy, these elements circulate. They move from nonliving materials into living things, back to nonliving, and so on, over and over again in great cycles. Ecologists call them *biogeochemical cycles.* "Bio" refers to living

organisms; "geo" to rocks, soils, water, and air; "chemical" to the changes that occur as the elements go through the cycles.

You probably already know about one of these cycles— the water cycle. Some scientists don't consider it to be a biogeochemical cycle because it involves the circulation of a compound of two elements, hydrogen and oxygen, rather than of a single element. Otherwise, the water cycle is like the others, with water moving from the atmosphere to the earth and living things and eventually back to the atmosphere.

There are two main types of biogeochemical cycle. In the gaseous type, the main storage area of an element is the earth's atmosphere, where it exists as a gas. Carbon and nitrogen have a gaseous cycle. Such cycles have little or no change in the abundance or distribution of their elements.

The earth's crust is the main storage area of the elements in the second type of cycle, the sedimentary cycle. Phosphorus and sulfur have sedimentary cycles. In these cycles, the abundance and distribution of an element may vary, for example when great amounts of phosphorus are deposited on the bottom of the ocean and stay there for millions of years.

A great deal of ecological research is now aimed at better understanding the biogeochemical cycles. Life can't exist without energy from the sun; neither can it exist without the cycling of elements from the earth, water, and air.

Sun energy powers the water cycle by evaporating water from the earth's surface, returning it to the atmosphere.

CARBON CYCLE

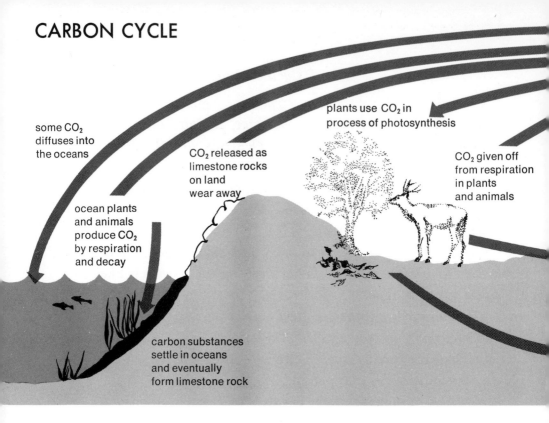

some CO₂ diffuses into the oceans

ocean plants and animals produce CO₂ by respiration and decay

CO₂ released as limestone rocks on land wear away

plants use CO₂ in process of photosynthesis

CO₂ given off from respiration in plants and animals

carbon substances settle in oceans and eventually form limestone rock

Three of the most important biogeochemical cycles are described and diagramed in this chapter. The diagrams are more simple than those you'll find in more advanced books on ecology. But whether simple or complex, a diagram is just a model of what ecologists believe happens in nature. No doubt the models of biogeochemical cycles will change as more is learned about the cycles.

THE CARBON CYCLE is the best known of the gaseous cycles. Most carbon is stored in the atmosphere and in the oceans as carbon dioxide. The carbon dioxide is taken up by green plants and is a vital material in the process of photosynthesis. Through this process the carbon

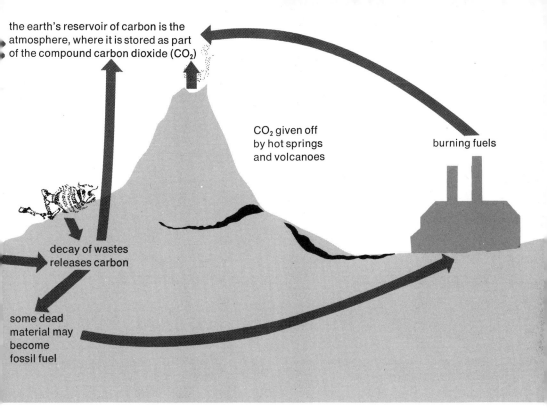

the earth's reservoir of carbon is the atmosphere, where it is stored as part of the compound carbon dioxide (CO_2)

CO_2 given off by hot springs and volcanoes

burning fuels

decay of wastes releases carbon

some dead material may become fossil fuel

atoms become part of molecules of simple carbohydrates, which later may be changed to fats, proteins, or more complex carbohydrates. From then on, carbon moves through ecosystems with the flow of energy, since energy is stored in the form of fats and carbohydrates. The carbon atoms travel along food chains, from plants to herbivores to carnivores, or to decomposers at any link along the way.

Digestion in animals breaks down molecules and the atoms from them recombine in many ways. A carbon atom might join with a calcium atom and three oxygen atoms to form a molecule of calcium carbonate. This molecule might stay in an animal's bone, breaking up only as the bone decayed after the animal's death. Other carbon atoms might leave an animal's body in a few hours' time, with its wastes.

Follow a carbon atom from swamp plants 300 million years ago . . .

to coal formed from the swamp plants . . .

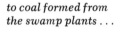

to an oak tree that takes in carbon dioxide given off by burning coal . . .

to the oak's acorns . . .

These pictures trace the possible route of a single carbon atom through time, as it is recycled in nature. Some of the carbon atoms in your body were once part of other living things, perhaps even of prehistoric animals such as dinosaurs.

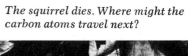

to a squirrel that eats the acorns.

The squirrel dies. Where might the carbon atoms travel next?

The burning of gasoline in automobiles releases great amounts of carbon dioxide and other waste gases into the atmosphere.

Many carbon atoms are returned to the atmosphere or to water in the form of carbon dioxide, which is released by plants and animals as a by-product of respiration, or "burning" food. But the greatest amount of carbon dioxide released into the atmosphere comes from dead plant and animal material as decomposers break it down. Of course, once a carbon dioxide molecule is released into the air, water, or soil, it may quickly become part of another living thing.

Throughout the history of the earth, some carbon has been withdrawn from the cycle when it became part of coal, oil, natural gas, peat, limestone, or coral reefs. Some of these carbon atoms are returned to the cycle when rain and wind wear down limestone rocks, or when volcanoes erupt. Until the last century or so, there was little return of the carbon that is locked up in deposits of coal, oil, and natural gas. But people have been burning ever increasing amounts of these fossil fuels, and are thus returning billions of tons of carbon dioxide to the carbon cycle. Some of it is absorbed by the oceans, but the amount of carbon dioxide in the atmosphere has increased by more than 12 per cent since 1880 and is expected to keep rising. The effects of this increase are still unknown. For a time it was feared that the increasing amounts of carbon dioxide were causing the entire atmosphere to grow warmer. Now, however, the atmosphere is getting cooler.

In laboratories and greenhouses, scientists have found that plants grow faster when the surrounding air is enriched with carbon dioxide. So the increase of this gas in the atmosphere may have raised the productivity of plants all over the world. So far, however, scientists have found no definite evidence that this has happened.

THE NITROGEN CYCLE has a huge store of this element in the atmosphere. About 78 per cent of the atmosphere is nitrogen. Each time you breathe, most of the gas that enters your lungs is nitrogen. But you breathe it out again, unused. The element nitrogen by itself is of no use to most living things. Combined with other elements, however, nitrogen is taken in by all life forms and is a vital part of proteins, perhaps the most important substances in living things.

The entire nitrogen cycle depends on a few kinds of bacteria, fungi, and blue-green algae that take nitrogen gas from the air and convert it to nitrogen compounds that can be used by themselves and other life. Some of these nitrogen-fixing organisms live freely in the soil; others live on the roots of plants such as beans, peas, alfalfa, clover, and vetch. In clover fields they fix as much as five hundred

NITROGEN CYCLE

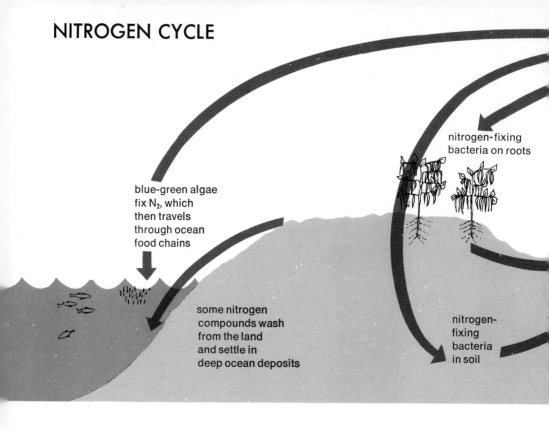

blue-green algae
fix N₂, which
then travels
through ocean
food chains

nitrogen-fixing
bacteria on roots

some nitrogen
compounds wash
from the land
and settle in
deep ocean deposits

nitrogen-
fixing
bacteria
in soil

pounds of nitrogen per acre. Some of the nitrogen compounds are given off into the soil. The rest become available to other kinds of plants when the nitrogen-fixing organisms die. Then the nitrogen compounds flow through food chains just as carbon does.

Dead plants and animals contain nitrogen compounds, and so do the body wastes of animals. As decomposers cause the decay of these materials, the nitrogen compounds are released and can be taken up immediately by green plants. In this way, nitrogen compounds can travel from the soil to plants to bacteria and back to the soil, cycling again and again without ever returning to the atmosphere as nitrogen gas. But the nitrogen cycle is complicated by

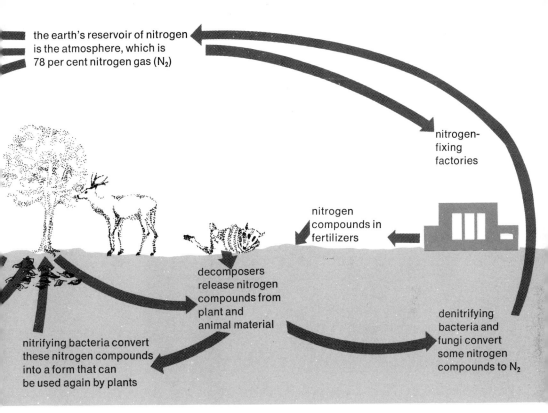

the earth's reservoir of nitrogen is the atmosphere, which is 78 per cent nitrogen gas (N_2)

nitrogen-fixing factories

nitrogen compounds in fertilizers

decomposers release nitrogen compounds from plant and animal material

denitrifying bacteria and fungi convert some nitrogen compounds to N_2

nitrifying bacteria convert these nitrogen compounds into a form that can be used again by plants

the existence of denitrifying bacteria and fungi, which break down nitrogen compounds and release nitrogen gas into the atmosphere. Of course, the nitrogen gas may later be captured by a nitrogen-fixing organism and join the earthbound part of the cycle again.

So far, humans seem to have had no noticeable effect on the nitrogen cycle. Although the body wastes of people and livestock, rich in nitrogen compounds, are mostly dumped into waterways and oceans rather than being recycled to the soil, man has learned how to take nitrogen gas from the air and "fix" it in compounds that are an important part of fertilizers. In 1968 alone, thirty million tons of nitrogen were converted for use in fertilizers. The amount fixed in-

PHOSPHORUS CYCLE

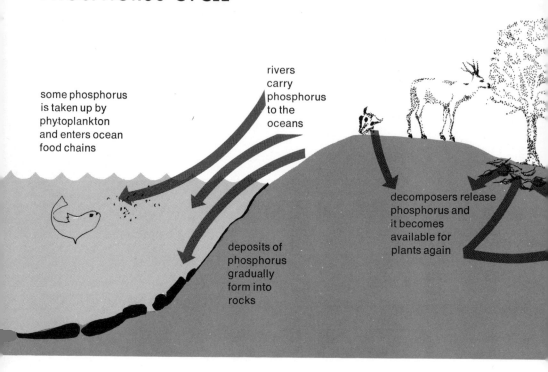

some phosphorus is taken up by phytoplankton and enters ocean food chains

rivers carry phosphorus to the oceans

deposits of phosphorus gradually form into rocks

decomposers release phosphorus and it becomes available for plants again

dustrially has been doubling every six years. Great amounts of these nitrogen compounds wash from the land and enrich the waters of lakes and rivers. Sometimes the waters are so enriched that there is too much plant growth and a loss of oxygen resulting in the death of fish and other animals (see pages 106–08).

No one knows whether man's activities will have an effect on the nitrogen cycle. There are still many blanks in our understanding of the cycle itself. This much is certain: Life can't exist without nitrogen, and the entire cycle depends on the "teamwork" of a variety of microscopic organisms that we know little about. These organisms are one of the most slender threads upon which all life hangs.

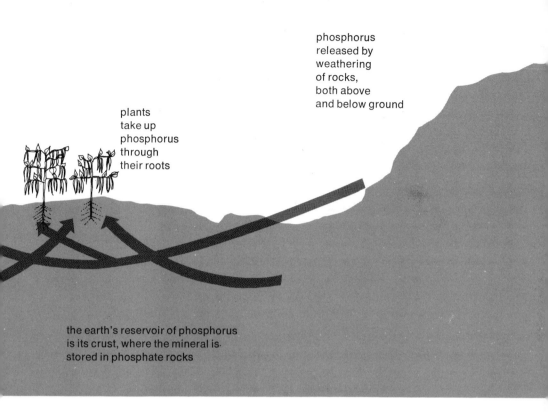

phosphorus released by weathering of rocks, both above and below ground

plants take up phosphorus through their roots

the earth's reservoir of phosphorus is its crust, where the mineral is stored in phosphate rocks

THE PHOSPHORUS CYCLE is an example of a sedimentary cycle, where the main storage of the element is in the earth's crust. Other elements that cycle in much the same way include calcium, iron, potassium, manganese, sodium, and sulfur. Some of these elements exist only in tiny amounts within living things, yet they are vital for normal growth and development. For example, no protein can be made without phosphorus and sulfur.

Phosphorus is one of the most important minerals ecologically. It is the one most likely to be in short supply. A lack of phosphorus causes low plant productivity and this, in turn, affects animal life. The phosphorus mineral is released from phosphate rocks as they are slowly broken up

Tobacco plant A received needed amounts of nitrogen,
phosphorus, potassium, boron, calcium and magnesium.
Compare its growth with that of the other tobacco
plants, each of which lacked one of these elements.

and worn away by the effects of raindrops, ice crystals,
wind, sunbeams, and plant roots. Then the phosphorus becomes a salt in solution, either in the soil water or in bodies
of water. Plants take up phosphorus and other mineral salts
through their roots. From plants, phosphorus passes
through various food chains, usually returning to the soil
or water through the actions of decomposers.

This is the salt-solution part of the cycle; the other part
might be called the rock phase. Rivers carry phosphorus
salts to the seas. Some are deposited in the shallows, where
they become part of sedimentary rocks that form over millions of years. Eventually the rocks become part of a new
land mass, producing new supplies of phosphorus salts as
they are slowly worn away. Phosphorus and many other
minerals are continually being formed into and freed from
rocks.

Upwelling currents bring some phosphorus up from the

ocean depths, and it is quickly taken in by phytoplankton and travels through ocean food chains. Some of this phosphorus is returned to the land through the harvest of fish. Some more comes from the guano (droppings) of fish-eating birds, which is rich in phosphorus and nitrogen. Guano is one of Peru's important natural resources, thanks to upwelling currents off the Peruvian coast which bring phosphorus and other nutrients to the surface. The nutrients are taken up by phytoplankton, which are eaten by tiny crustaceans, which are eaten by fish called anchovies, which are eaten by seabirds called cormorants. These birds nest in enormous numbers on islands and their droppings are harvested and sold as an ingredient of fertilizers.

Harvesting guano on an island off the Peruvian coast

Most of the phosphorus used in fertilizers is quarried from phosphate rocks. Vast amounts of phosphorus are spread on the land, and many tons wash away and are lost to the depths of the sea. An estimated three and a half billion tons of phosphorus are lost each year in this way, and the natural recycling from the seas cannot match this loss. There are still many years' supply of phosphate rocks left for use in fertilizer but the supply is limited; someday man may have to find a way to retrieve phosphorus from the ocean depths.

Humans have added some entirely new materials to biogeochemical cycles. Elements such as strontium, barium, and cesium have been released into the atmosphere from nuclear power plants and from tests of nuclear weapons. Some of these elements remain radioactive for thousands of years. They get into food chains and become part of plants and animals. Because they are radioactive they may damage living things in a variety of ways. The long-range effects are unknown, but are of great concern to ecologists and other scientists.

One of the most important radioactive elements released into biogeochemical cycles is strontium-90. It is a common by-product of atomic explosions and is part of atomic wastes from nuclear power plants. It loses its radioactivity slowly. In nature, it behaves like calcium and is quickly taken up by plants through their leaves and roots. When taken in with food by humans and other vertebrates, it becomes concentrated in their bones, just as calcium is. There has been a small but steady buildup of strontium-90 in the bones of people in North America and Europe. The concentrations are greatest in people of the tundra, Eskimos and Laplanders.

Ecologists have found unusual amounts of another radioactive element, cesium-137, in the bodies of some Alaskan Eskimos. They found that these Eskimos had eaten a lot of caribou meat. The caribou feed mostly on the lichens that are so abundant on the tundra. And the lichens absorb the cesium-137 when it settles out of the atmosphere from some faraway source. The cesium becomes more and more concentrated as it travels through food chains. Ecologists found that caribou had as much as three times the concen-

Caribou feed mostly on tundra lichens which may contain cesium-137 and strontium-90.

tration of cesium as lichens. The Eskimos had twice as much of the concentration as the caribou.

People release other substances into nature which become more concentrated as they move along in food chains. Insect poisons such as DDT travel through food chains and biogeochemical cycles. When this long-lasting biocide ("life killer") is sprayed, some of the poison particles may be carried hundreds or thousands of miles through the atmosphere. DDT is also washed from the land by rainfall, just as fertilizers are. Then it becomes part of food chains in the water.

DDT has been found in the bodies of Antarctic penguins. It is reducing the numbers of the Bermuda petrel, a rare species of seabird. The petrel feeds at sea and visits Ber-

muda only to breed. Nevertheless, DDT was found in unhatched eggs and in dead chicks. The nearest source of the biocide was farmland in the United States, six hundred and fifty miles away. The DDT apparently ran off the land with rainwater, then reached the petrels through ocean food chains.

The element mercury is sometimes released into the environment as waste from incinerators, paper mills, chemical industries, and from the burning of fuels. Then it travels through food chains in the water. In 1970, dangerous amounts of mercury were found in fish from many North American lakes.

Ecologists sometimes put small amounts of radioactive materials into nature so that they can trace the materials through cycles and food chains. The accidental releases of materials such as strontium-90, DDT, and mercury have been similar, giant "tracer experiments," with damaging and potentially disastrous results. People continue to·release all sorts of new chemical compounds into nature without having any idea of how long the substances last, where they go, or what effects they have on living things. To begin to answer these questions, ecologists must first learn much more about the great cycles of the world ecosystem.

Animals at the end of food chains, particularly eagles and other birds of prey, are endangered by such biocides as DDT.

6

Everything Changes

LAKE ERIE IS DYING . . .
DEATH OF A GREAT LAKE . . .
LAKE ERIE: A DEAD SEA

You may have read headlines like these in newspapers or seen reports on television about Lake Erie. The lake is far from dead, but it is amazing even to think of this big lake—almost ten thousand square miles in size—being in danger of dying.

Actually, only the speed of Lake Erie's death is amazing. All lakes and ponds die. They begin to age as soon as they are born. The death of lakes and ponds is a natural process, part of the inevitable change that goes on in nature all the time. Usually the changes follow a regular pattern, with one stage following, or succeeding, another. Ecologists call these changes *succession.*

There are two main types of succession. Primary succession is slow to get started. It occurs in areas where life

does not already exist—on land newly exposed by a retreating glacier, in a newly formed lake or pond, on a vol-
canic island just thrust up from the sea floor. The island
called Surtsey, formed by a volcano off the coast of Ice-

Surtsey rose in the North Atlantic Ocean in 1963.

These drawings show how a lake goes through a series of changes over thousands of years, finally becoming dry land.

land in 1963, has given ecologists a great and rare opportunity to observe primary succession.

Secondary succession occurs in areas where existing plant-animal communities have been disturbed or almost destroyed in some way. Even as the ashes of a forest fire cool, new life in the form of sprouting seeds and still-living roots begins to change the area back into a forest. In the same way, almost any place—a vacant lot, a newly dredged pond, or your back yard—if left alone, goes through a series of changes in plant and animal life. In most of North America, the land would eventually be covered with a forest, if succession were allowed to occur.

Primary succession in Lake Erie began more than twelve thousand years ago, when a retreating glacier left a huge basin in the land. Water from the melting glacier filled the basin and Lake Erie was born. At first its waters were clear, cold, and almost lifeless. In the first, or pioneer, stage of succession the bottom of a lake or pond is barren of plant life. The earliest forms of life are plankton.

As water flows into a lake or pond from the surrounding countryside, it carries particles of soil and dead leaves which settle to the bottom. Plants along the shore also add once-living material to the lake or pond. In Lake Erie, some of this material was carried away by the Niagara River, but most of it stayed. Ever so slowly, the lake became shallower. As decomposers broke down the detritus, the lake also became rich in minerals and other nutrients.

This enrichment of a body of water is called *eutrophication*. A eutrophic lake is well fed with minerals such as

Great growths of algae float in the shore waters of the lake at the left. Fish called bullheads are another sign of a eutrophic lake.

phosphorus and nitrogen. As a lake becomes more eutrophic, it supports more plant and animal life. This, in turn, adds more detritus to the lake bottom, making it shallower. As more and more plants and animals die, the filling of the lake speeds up. The lake shrinks in size. Eventually it becomes a shallow marsh. The marsh itself fills and then there is dry land where the waters of a wide, blue lake once shone in the sunlight.

A big lake usually lives for thousands of years. A small pond may pass from birth to death in a hundred years. The speed of "death" depends on the amount of minerals entering the lake, how much detritus is carried away through the outlet, and on the size and depth of the body of water. Deep lakes die very slowly, because sunlight doesn't reach their depths and algae can't produce food there. A lake ages more quickly as it gets shallower and sunlight can reach the bottom everywhere.

Lake Erie is the oldest and shallowest of the Great Lakes, so it is natural that it is aging faster than the others. However, its death is being speeded by pollution. The lake is enriched with wastes from industries and sewage from houses. Rain washes fertilizers off the land from farms and lawns. Phosphorus enters the lake in waste water containing detergents. People are unintentionally making the lake incredibly rich for plant life and are thereby hastening its death. One biologist estimates that man's effects on Lake Erie have shortened its life by fifteen thousand years—so far.

The plentiful plant foods in Lake Erie have produced great growths of algae and other water plants. When the plants die they settle to the bottom along with sewage and other once-living material. Ordinarily they would decay there. But the process of decay requires oxygen, and in parts of Lake Erie there is so much waste that most or all of the oxygen is taken from the water. Then most decay stops and the wastes just keep piling up on the bottom.

The animal life in a lake or pond is affected when decay robs its waters of oxygen. In Lake Erie the fish that are considered best for food are disappearing. Some of the loss is caused by overfishing, but the eutrophic conditions are mostly to blame. Herring, whitefish, and blue pike, which need oxygen-rich water, are being replaced by fish like carp and perch, which can live in water containing less oxygen.

Lake Erie is only one of thousands of lakes and ponds in North America that are being affected in the same way. It may be natural for lakes to die, but the way people are treating these beautiful and valuable waters, it seems more like murder.

With or without the influence of people, primary succession takes a long time. Secondary succession, wherever it occurs, produces changes that you can see in just a few years' time. You can observe these changes on abandoned farm land, in vacant lots, and along roadsides.

Succession on abandoned land has been studied in several areas in the United States. Here is what might happen on an abandoned field in the southeast:

The land isn't bare for long. Crabgrass, horseweed, and other pioneer plants soon cover the ground. Some plants sprout from roots already in the soil; others from seeds carried to the field by wind or birds. In the second year, asters and ragweed become common in the field. The pioneer plants grow best on bare, sun-drenched soil. The kinds of plants that follow the pioneers have seeds that sprout and grow well in the shade of the pioneers. The new arrivals eventually crowd out the pioneers by shading them from the sun. In this way the asters help eliminate the horseweeds. By the third summer, a tall bunchgrass called broomsedge appears and begins taking over.

Broomsedges are the dominant plants for several years, but pines—the next stage in succession—appear as seedlings among the sedges. Pine seedlings need almost full sunlight to grow well, and they struggle for a few years in the shade of the sedges. Once above them, they grow quickly, shading out the sedges and other field plants that need a lot of sunlight. Soon a young pine forest covers the land.

Perhaps a century after a field was abandoned, a tall pine forest grows on it. But this is not the end of succes-

Secondary succession on a bare field may follow many patterns, but in much of North America the final stage is a forest. If the forest is felled or burned, the succession starts all over again.

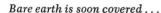
Bare earth is soon covered ...

by plants that thrive in the open ...

but they are eventually shaded out by taller plants ...

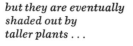

form a forest.

including young trees,
which after many years . . .

sion. Normally a pine forest does not replace itself. Pine seedlings can't grow well in the dense shade of the evergreen forest, and the adult trees compete with the seedlings for water. Other kinds of trees can survive under these conditions, however, and saplings of sweet gum, red maple, oak, and hickory begin to grow beneath the pines. As the old pines die, they are replaced by the deciduous trees, especially by oaks and hickories. After two hundred years or so, an oak-hickory forest covers what was once a bare field.

Ecologists call the last stage of succession a *climax*. It is usually stable and may change little for centuries if undisturbed. Everything changes in nature, however, and ecologists doubt whether any such thing as a truly permanent climax really exists.

The succession from bare field to oak-hickory forest described above is probably an accurate picture of what happens in some parts of the southeastern United States. But plant succession in an area is affected by many factors, including climate, soils, animals, and the availability of different kinds of plant seeds. Climate certainly plays a big part. In the dry Western plains, succession leads to a grass climax after twenty to forty years. Succession is greatly affected by living things, with plants themselves affecting the climate at ground level, sometimes enabling the next stage of plant life to get started.

In one small valley, succession may differ between the north- and south-facing slopes, and between the slopes and the valley floor. Some stages may be skipped, or may last far longer on one site than on another. The old idea that succession is an orderly and predictable step-by-step process has been discarded. Once more, we have discovered that nature is more complex than we first thought.

Although ecologists have studied succession in many parts of the world, mostly they have just described the changes in plant and animal life that occur. They have found that the kinds of organisms change continuously, and that the species that are important in the early stages aren't likely to be important in the climax stage. Recently ecologists have begun investigating the effects of succession on the flow of energy and the production of biomass. Ecologists are especially curious about the stability of the climax stage, and what keeps it stable. The widely accepted theory is that stability in nature is a result of diversity. In other words, the more varied a community's plant and animal life, the more stable or resistant to change it will be. Diversity includes both the number of species and the number of individuals of each species.

The most diverse communities on earth are probably the climax tropical rain forests. In Colombia, for example, there are nearly 1,400 species of nesting birds, compared with 195 in New York State and 56 in Greenland. In the rain forests, if one kind of plant or animal were completely wiped out, there would probably be no noticeable effects on the community. In other, simpler communities, the loss of one plant or animal species could have far-reaching effects. In the tundra, for example, caribou feed mostly on a lichen called reindeer moss. The loss of this one kind of plant would seriously affect caribou and the animals that depend on them for food.

The stability of communities is of vital interest to man. All over the earth, people are simplifying ecosystems. Vast areas have no stable climax communities. Instead, succession has been set back or halted by man. Fire, lumbering, and farming all destroy climax communities. Then man tries to hold back succession in order to raise crops and livestock, or to modify nature for some other reason. Millions of acres around homes and schools are maintained as lawns—a pioneer stage of succession—simply because many people find them pleasing to look at.

Farm crops are very simple plant communities. The

Wheat, corn, and other crop lands are maintained as simple plant-animal communities through use of man's machinery and chemicals.

plants couldn't survive without help from man. This help, in the form of cultivation, and weed and pest killers, reduces the diversity of the community even further. The so-called pest killers, in particular, simplify animal communities. They kill not only pests but many harmless species of insects and even the insects that normally prey on pests. The result is a very artificial, simple community, one that is ripe for the quick spread of a pest or disease.

The challenge of maintaining stability in ecosystems is being studied a great deal by ecologists. For his food production, man will probably always have to keep a lot of land in early stages of succession. But it may be desirable to increase the diversity of cropland communities. Many of man's ideas about agriculture haven't changed much since farming began thousands of years ago. Perhaps these ideas will change as ecologists learn more about succession and the stability of plant-animal communities.

7

Patterns in Populations

A female housefly produces an average of 120 eggs at a time. One fly can produce seven generations a year, and half of the eggs develop into females. If all of the individual females survive and reproduce in each generation, there would be over 6,000,000,000,000 flies at the end of the year.

This illustrates the ability of houseflies to reproduce, or their *biotic potential*. Any population of organisms, whether dandelions, bullfrogs, or houseflies, has great biotic potential. But we are not up to our thighs in frogs or flies. Some factors in nature keep the populations from reaching their potential. These factors are called the *environmental resistance*. They include disease, predators, competition, weather—any factor that checks population

A dandelion has great biotic potential.

Spiders are part of the environmental resistance to the biotic potential of flies and other insects.

growth. The human population has increased greatly because people have found ways to reduce environmental resistance, especially through disease control. After malaria was brought under control in Guyana the human population increased 62 per cent in just seven years.

Most populations in nature do not show such big rises, or great falls. There is usually a balance between the biotic potential and the environmental resistance and the population stays about the same from year to year. When the balance goes awry, it is an unusual event.

Ecologists began studying animal populations early in this century. They have learned a great deal but much remains to be discovered. In recent years population studies

have taken on greater importance because of concern
about the rapidly rising number of humans.

Population is usually defined as the number of organisms of one kind that occupy a certain area at a certain
time. For example, there were nearly 205,000,000 people
living in the United States in 1970.

The most direct method of finding the total population is
to count every individual. In the winter, you could make
several flights over Isle Royale National Park in Lake

*Sampling the fish population of a stream, an ecologist uses a device
to temporarily stun the fish so they can be examined.*

Superior and probably get an accurate count of its wolf and moose population. Elsewhere, you could use aerial photographs to get an accurate count of the number of migratory geese and ducks resting on a lake.

Usually a total count of a population is impossible, however, so ecologists take samples of the population and from them try to make some generalizations about the entire population. This is fairly easy to do with populations of plants, which don't move about, but more difficult with animals.

Some important discoveries about populations have been made in laboratories, where biologists have observed changes in numbers of water fleas, yeast cells, and algae cells. The populations of these organisms grew slowly at first, then increased rapidly, then leveled or dropped off. Ecologists have noticed the same pattern in studies of wild animals. Once a population reaches a certain level, it usually stays about the same from year to year, unless the environment changes a great deal. If a population does rise or fall greatly over a span of time, the changes are often part of a regular pattern or cycle.

Population cycles are most common in the simpler ecosystems of the world, especially in the northern taiga and tundra. There the numbers of certain animals rise for several years, then drop sharply. This happens again and again, usually over a span of nine or ten years. A population cycle shows up well in the numbers of Canada lynx, a wild cat that weighs about twenty-five pounds.

The ups and downs of lynx numbers are probably caused

GROWTH CURVE OF YEAST CELLS

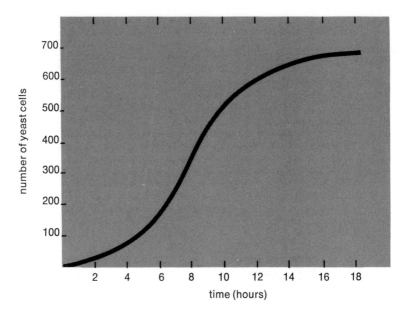

Populations in laboratories and in the wild often follow this pattern, rising rapidly for a time, then leveling off.

GROWTH CURVES OF TWO SPECIES OF GOLDEN-BROWN ALGAE

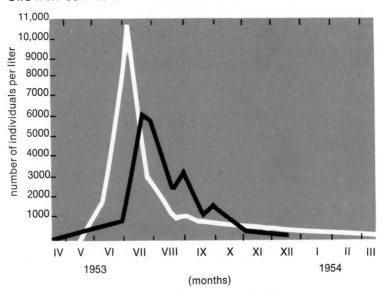

Some populations grow very rapidly, then die off. This pattern occurs among such organisms as insects and plants that live for just one growing season, and among other organisms that exhaust the resources in their environments.

GRAPH OF LYNX POPULATION

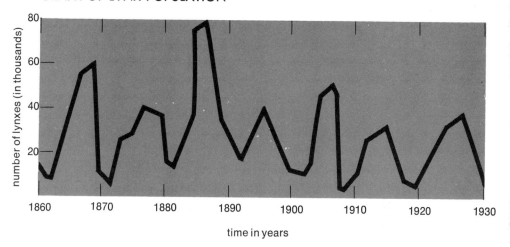

by changes in the population of snowshoe hares, which lynx eat. The hares are the main food of the lynx, so a change in the hare population can greatly affect the numbers of lynx. But why do the numbers of hares go up and down over a span of ten years? Ecologists have some ideas about this but it is a puzzle that is far from solved.

The size of most populations remains remarkably constant year after year. Many factors in the environment work together to keep the population in check. In the laboratory, ecologists found that small mammals called meadow voles produced more young when they had plenty of sodium in their diet. Checking this idea further, ecologists in the field discovered that the most abundant vole populations were in areas with plentiful sodium in the soil. Where soil sodium was low, the vole populations were low.

Weather can also affect animal populations. Heavy spring rains may cause the death of young pheasants,

quail, and rabbits. Late spring floods may drown young muskrats, and force the adults to areas where predators catch them easily. A drought in a muskrat marsh has the same effect. With the protection of water gone, muskrats are more easily caught by foxes, mink, and other predators.

Mostly, however, populations are kept in check by living rather than nonliving factors. For some species, the main limiting factor is predation. On Isle Royale, a population of about twenty wolves preys on moose, limiting the herd to about six hundred animals. Since wolves and other big predators have been wiped out in many parts of North America, food supply has become the main limiting factor on populations of deer and other large hoofed animals.

Predators sometimes control populations of small mammals. In Georgia, Dr. Jay H. Schnell put large numbers of cotton rats into two fenced-in areas. One area was designed so that no hawks, foxes, or other predators could get in. Dr. Schnell then observed the cotton rat populations in each area.

Few rats died in the protected area. In the unprotected one, the population dropped until it was about the same as that normally found on a similar-sized area in the wild. The protected area supported five times as many rats as the unprotected area. So Dr. Schnell concluded that in the wild there would be many more cotton rats if it weren't for predators.

Many animal populations are preyed upon but are not

Deer often starve to death in areas lacking large predators.

controlled by predation. This seems to be the case with muskrats. The late Dr. Paul Errington studied muskrats in Iowa for over forty years. He found that predators, especially mink, often killed great numbers of muskrats. But Dr. Errington learned that mink killed mostly the "extra" animals—those that did not have a safe place in the population. These animals died even if there were no mink or other predators around. Disease killed them, or they died fighting among themselves, or of starvation, or from exposure to weather.

Some populations are controlled by parasites. The most striking examples of the effect of a parasite are those where a parasite is introduced to an area where it never lived before. The American chestnut tree has been almost completely wiped out by a parasitic fungus from Asia. Many elms have been killed by another fungus introduced in the 1920s from Europe. In both cases, the fungus was a control on tree populations in its native land but did not drastically reduce the numbers of the trees. In North America, the chestnuts and elms had no resistance to the parasites, unlike the trees in the native lands of the parasites. Normally, a parasite or predator doesn't eliminate the population on which it depends for life.

Animal and plant populations are often kept in check by *competition,* when two organisms strive for some necessity for life that is not in adequate supply for both. Competition is greatest within a species, since all individuals have the same basic needs. On a walk in a woods you may see thousands of oak and maple seedlings on the forest floor.

Ecologists have examined the remains of moose killed by wolves and found that many of these animals were weakened by parasites or disease. This made them easier prey than healthy moose.

They compete with each other for sunlight, minerals, and water. Only a few will survive to become adult trees. It would be impossible for all of the seedlings to become trees because there simply aren't enough resources—not even enough space—to go around.

Each spring we hear the songs of birds, another example of competition within a species. A male bird sings to establish a territory where he and his mate will nest. The male defends the territory against other males of the same species, and only those individuals that have territories breed and raise young. This behavior pattern in birds and in some kinds of mammals helps a species avoid direct competition for food and other necessities.

Different kinds of plants and animals also compete with one another. From experiments with flour beetles and protozoa, ecologists have concluded that no two species can indefinitely continue to occupy the same niche. In nature, two species may be nearly alike in most ways but have different feeding habits, use different foods, or feed at different times or places (see pages 18–21). In this way they avoid direct competition for food. In times of food shortage, however, they may compete. Snowshoe hares and moose share most of the same food plants in Newfoundland. Sometimes the moose eat so much of the plant growth close to the ground that the hares don't have enough food or places to hide.

Some of the most fascinating and least understood of all

A variety of plants compete for light on the forest floor.

the limiting factors on populations take effect when a population reaches a certain density and the animals sense that they are crowded. Laboratory populations of water fleas, flour beetles, mice, rats, and other animals all produced fewer young when they became crowded. In mammals, the crowding seemed to produce a nervous condition called stress which then caused changes in certain glands. The glands, in turn, affected the reproduction and behavior of the mammals.

In a laboratory experiment where rats were crowded together, the females had fewer young than normal, and many young died before birth. When young were born alive, the mother rats often abandoned or ate them. More rats than usual died of disease. Ecologists have noticed the same sort of effects of crowding in wild populations of jackrabbits, snowshoe hares, voles, and deer.

Population studies are one of the most exciting and active fields of ecology today. Old ideas are being challenged and new questions asked. For example, does crowding have any effects on people similar to those noticed in other mammals? The rapid growth of human population can't be ignored, and many of the biological forces that affect mice, rabbits, and deer also affect humans.

The world population doubled in the period from 1750 to 1900, or in 150 years. It doubled again by 1965. It is expected to double again—to seven billion—by the year 2000, just thirty-five years from 1965. Unless population growth slows drastically, the total number of people on earth will keep doubling at an ever faster pace.

Smallpox vaccinations have reduced the environmental resistance of disease on human populations.

People are demonstrating their tremendous biotic potential now that the environmental resistance of food shortages and diseases has lessened. So far, the world's food supply has increased along with population, although many people are poorly fed and some still starve to death. Looking into the future though, ecologists know that the human population must stop increasing and level off, just as all animal populations do. The earth is limited in size, in farmland, and in the amount of food that can be grown on land and in the sea. From their studies of animal populations, ecologists know that if human numbers keep rising, some factor in the environment such as disease, lack of food, or lack of space will eventually halt that growth.

Dr. Thomas Park, a zoologist at the University of Chicago, who studies animal populations, has said, "If man does not manage *his* biology, *it* will manage him."

8
Science of Survival

All organisms cause changes in their environment, but only humans have the power to wipe out all other life on the earth and destroy the very environment on which they depend. Plans are being made to change the weather over large areas, to reshape great river systems, to dump vast amounts of poisonous wastes into the oceans. Meanwhile, other "insults" to ecosystems go on: pollution, erosion, biocide poisoning, and the destruction of rain forests, estuaries, and other highly productive ecosystems which we know so little about.

However, people are beginning to realize that nature is not an adversary to be conquered. Man is just one thread in the web of life. As an ecologist recently wrote: "The object of man's game with nature is not to win, but to keep on playing."

Humans can't escape from their dependence on the
earth. Even when astronauts venture into the universe,
they must take a fragment of the earth's ecosystem with
them. Their lives depend on the water, air, and food
brought from the earth.

"When we try to pick out something by itself, we find it hitched to everything else in the universe." These words, written many years ago by John Muir, express a lesson for man today. People can no longer ignore their dependence on nature, nor the inevitable side effects that occur when

An open pit mine in British Columbia illustrates the great changes man makes in ecosystems.

they make changes in ecosystems. One example of these side effects occurred in Borneo recently. Great quantities of DDT were sprayed in a mosquito control campaign. The biocide was effective and killed many mosquitoes. However, it also killed great numbers of predatory wasps. The wasps had been a control on the numbers of certain caterpillars. The caterpillars increased (they were not harmed by the DDT). Soon the thatched roofs of the natives' houses began to fall in because they were being eaten by the caterpillars.

The ecological side effects went on, because DDT was also sprayed indoors to control houseflies. Normally the houseflies were eaten by geckos, and these lizards began to die when they ate the poisoned flies. Then the geckos were eaten by house cats. The cats received all of the DDT concentrated from the flies and geckos. They died in such numbers that rats began to invade the houses and eat food. Rats in Borneo sometimes carry a deadly disease called plague. The authorities became so alarmed that they parachuted a new supply of cats into the area as a first step in restoring the balance in an ecosystem they had upset by spraying DDT.

This chain of events illustrates how living things depend on each other, and how man's ignorance about ecology leads to troubles for himself and other living things. People are learning: When you insult nature, you can expect to be slapped back. For humans to survive on earth, they will always have to change ecosystems to meet their needs for food, shelter, and other necessities. But ecological insults can be kept to a minimum; changes can be made with

The radio collar on this snowshoe hare sends signals that reveal the animal's location and activities.

forethought and understanding. If this isn't done, some scientists warn, humans may destroy their life-giving environment before the end of this century. No wonder ecology has been called "the science of survival."

Just a few decades ago, ecology was a sort of "car window botany," with ecologists still describing the world of nature in a general way. The science has made great strides since then. Now ecologists make mathematical models of ecosystems and use computers to try to predict the effects of changes in real ecosystems. They have accurate, portable devices that automatically measure and record the flow of energy and materials in an environment. Tiny radio transmitters can be put on wild animals. The radio signals are then received by a computer that records information about the animals' locations and activities.

Ecologists can measure the annual energy input in a large ecosystem like a lake. They can discover how much energy goes to melt ice, to warm the water, to power living

Ecologists studying the energy production of the grassland biome

things. They are now beginning to be able to predict the effects that would occur if various changes were made in the lake. In a few years they may be able to do this with more complex ecosystems—forests, deserts, entire river valleys.

Ecologists know, however, how short a distance their science has come. They know what tremendous problems they will be expected to solve. It has been said that ecology will be *the* science of the twenty-first century. Even before then, however, ecologists must help solve scores of environmental problems—slowing the death of lakes from eutrophication, finding safe alternatives to biocides, maintaining the stability of ecosystems, and designing more livable cities, to name a few.

These problems are difficult, and solutions to them will involve all of science. To solve them, we will have to use every bit of our understanding of the world ecosystem. It is really much easier to build a telescope to look at stars or to build a rocket to land on Mars than it is to understand the land and life around us. And the impact of man on the earth ecosystem has been so destructive in so many ways that if we do not give much more attention to understanding the web of nature, we are not going to be here to build telescopes or to wonder about Mars.

Although ecology is a science, the wisdom of it can and should have effects on man's basic values. There must be a rethinking of man's place in nature, and of his attitudes toward it. If man is to survive, he must develop an ecological conscience, with love, respect, and understanding for the earth ecosystem of which he is a part.

Glossary

Ecology Vocabulary

ADAPTATION—a characteristic of an organism that improves its chance of surviving in its environment; for example, the breeding behavior of the grunion, the water-storing capacity of a cactus.

ALGAE—a group of plants lacking roots, stems, and leaves, including long seaweeds and tiny one-celled forms. It is the microscopic blue-green algae that often become too abundant in eutrophic waters.

ATOM—the smallest particle of an element.

BACTERIA—one-celled microscopic organisms (usually classified as plants); some cause diseases, many are decomposers.

BIOCIDE—a poison or other substance used to kill such pests as injurious insects, but which also kills useful insects and other living things.

BIOGEOCHEMICAL CYCLES—the movements of minerals and other elements through the living and nonliving parts of ecosystems.

BIOMASS—the total weight of living organisms in a given area, often expressed in grams per square meter.

BIOME—a major land ecosystem that has a distinct kind of plant life, such as grassland or tropical rain forest.

BIOSPHERE—the thin skin of soil, water, and air where life exists on the earth.

BIOTIC POTENTIAL—the ability of a species or of a population to increase its numbers. Factors in the environment such as disease and predators usually keep a population from reaching its biotic potential.

CANOPY—in a forest, the upper layer, formed by the leaves and branches of the tallest trees.

CARBOHYDRATES—sugars, starches, and cellulose; carbohydrates are compounds made up of the elements hydrogen, oxygen, and carbon.

CARNIVORE—an animal that eats the flesh of other animals.

CLIMATE—the average weather conditions of an area, including temperature, precipitation, humidity, windiness, and hours of sunlight.

CLIMAX—the last and most stable stage in succession.

COMMENSALISM—a symbiotic association between two dissimilar organisms, in which one benefits and the other is usually unaffected. See SYMBIOSIS.

COMMUNITY—all of the plants and animals in a particular environment.

COMPETITION—the striving of different organisms for the same food, water, minerals, sunlight, or other necessity for life that is not in adequate supply for all of them.

COMPOUND—a distinct substance formed by the combination of two or more elements in definite proportions.

CONSUMERS—organisms that get their food energy from other living things.

DECIDUOUS—having leaves of a type that fall off all in one season, usually autumn.

DECOMPOSERS—plants and animals that feed on once-living material and cause it to mechanically or chemically break down.

DETRITUS—dead plant and animal material; it is the source of food energy for decomposers and for many consumers.

ECOLOGY—the study of the relationships between living things and their environment.

ECOSYSTEM—all of the living and nonliving parts of a given area in nature. Ecosystems range in size from puddles to oceans; from a single acorn to a huge forest.

ECOTONE—the place where two ecosystems or biomes meet and blend together; for example, the shore of a pond.

ELEMENT—a distinct variety of matter consisting of atoms of only one kind. It cannot be broken down by ordinary chemical and physical processes. Examples include oxygen, calcium, sodium, iron, hydrogen, lead.

ENVIRONMENT—all of the surroundings of an organism, including other living things, climate, soil.

ENVIRONMENTAL RESISTANCE—the factors in an environment that keep a species or population from increasing to its full biotic potential. The factors include competition, disease, predators, parasites, and the effects of crowding.

EPIPHYTES—plants that have a commensal relationship with other plants, depending on them for physical support but not harming them in any way.

ESTIVATION—a prolonged sleeplike state that enables an animal to survive during the summer months in a hot climate. As in hibernation, the animal's body processes, such as breathing and heartbeat, slow down drastically.

ESTUARY—a place where salt water and fresh water mix, usually where a river enters an ocean.

ETHOLOGY—the study of animal behavior.

EUTROPHICATION—the process by which a body of water becomes enriched with minerals and other nutrients.

FOOD CHAIN—the passage of food energy through a series of organisms, for example, from grass to mouse to fox.

FOOD WEB—a system of interlocking food chains; the total pattern of all of the separate food chains in a community.

FUNGI—a group of simple plants lacking roots, stems, leaves, and the green-coloring substance chlorophyll. Fungi and bacteria are the main decomposers in nature.

GUANO—the body wastes (droppings) of seabirds and of bats. Guano deposits are "mined" for use as fertilizers.

HABITAT—the living place, or immediate surroundings of an organism.

HERBIVORE—an animal that eats mostly plants.

IRRIGATION—supplying land with water, usually through use of canals, ditches, flooding, or spraying.

KILOCALORIE—a unit of energy; the amount of heat needed to raise the temperature of one liter of water one degree centigrade.

KINETIC ENERGY—energy of motion.

METEOROLOGY—the study of the earth's atmosphere, including weather and climate.

MINERAL—a naturally occurring nonliving substance composed of one element or several elements and having definite chemical and physical characteristics.

MOLECULE—the smallest possible amount of an element or compound that still "acts" like larger amounts of the substance.

MUTUALISM—a symbiotic association between two dissimilar organisms in which both partners benefit. See SYMBIOSIS.

NET PRODUCTIVITY—see PRODUCTIVITY.

NICHE—the role an organism plays in nature, its "occupation" in the community.

NUTRIENT—a substance needed for normal growth and development of an organism.

OMNIVORE—an animal that eats both plants and animals.

PARASITISM—a symbiotic association between two dissimilar organisms in which one organism lives on or in the other (its host), harming it but usually not killing it.

PERMAFROST—permanently frozen ground, occurring in the Arctic.

PHOTOSYNTHESIS—the process by which green plants convert carbon dioxide and water into simple sugars. The process is powered by radiant energy from the sun and occurs only in the presence of the green-coloring substance chlorophyll.

PHYTOPLANKTON—see PLANKTON.

PLANKTON—tiny, drifting plants and animals that live in salt and fresh water. The plant, or phytoplankton, include diatoms and algae. The animal, or zooplankton, include rotifers and copepods.

POLLUTION—man-produced wastes that lower the quality of the environment.

POPULATION—the number of individuals of a certain species that live in a particular area at a particular time; for example, the number of people in the United States in 1975.

POTENTIAL ENERGY—stored energy; energy that is released from matter only when the matter is changed in some way.

PREDATOR—an animal that kills other animals for food.

PRODUCERS—organisms in a community that convert radiant energy from the sun into food energy that can be used by consumers.

PRODUCTIVITY—the total amount of living matter produced by a plant, population, or an entire community; this amount is often called the gross productivity. Some of this material is used by the organisms themselves. The remaining material is available to other organisms and is called the net productivity.

PROTEIN—the nutrient needed for proper growth and development. Proteins make up three quarters of the dry weight of the human body.

RADIANT ENERGY—energy given off by the sun. Only part of it is visible, but it is this visible part (sunlight) that provides the energy on which all living things depend.

RADIOACTIVITY—a property of some elements by which the center (nucleus) of an atom breaks up by emitting particles. These radioactive particles can't be seen or felt but may harm living things.

RESPIRATION—the process of "burning" food, in which bound energy is released for use by an organism. In this cellular process, oxygen is consumed and carbon dioxide is given off as a waste. Respiration occurs in both plants and animals.

SILT—soil made up of fine particles (finer than sand); carried along by currents, silt settles to the bottom in quiet waters.

SUCCESSION—the process in which a plant-animal community is replaced by another, then another, and so on, as in the change from a bare field to a mature forest.

SYMBIOSIS—"living together"; a close association between two dissimilar organisms in a relationship that may benefit both, one, or neither. See COMMENSALISM; MUTUALISM; PARASITISM.

TOPOGRAPHY—the shape of the land, including features such as hills, valleys, streams, and lakes.

WATERSHED—the area from which water drains into a pond, lake, or stream. The watershed of the Mississippi River covers 1,250,000 square miles. The watershed of a small pond might cover only a few acres or less.

ZOOPLANKTON—see PLANKTON.

Further Reading

Books marked with an asterisk (*) are fairly simple; the others are more difficult. Books marked with a dagger (†) are also available in paperback.

GENERAL ECOLOGY

ALLEE, W. C., et al., *Principles of Animal Ecology*. Philadelphia: W. B. Saunders Company, 1949.

†BILLINGS, W. D., *Plants and the Ecosystem*. Belmont, Calif.: Wadsworth Publishing Company, Inc., 1964.

*†BUCHSBAUM, RALPH and MILDRED, *Basic Ecology*. Pittsburgh: The Boxwood Press, 1957.

*DARLING, LOIS and LOUIS, *A Place in the Sun*. New York: William Morrow and Company, 1968.

ELTON, CHARLES, *The Ecology of Animals* (3rd edn.). New York: John Wiley & Sons, Inc., 1950.

*FARB, PETER, and the Editors of *Life*, *Ecology*. New York: Time, Inc., 1963.

HANDLER, PHILIP, ed., *Biology and the Future of Man*. New York: Oxford University Press, 1970, pp. 431–473.

*HIRSCH, S. CARL, *The Living Community: A Venture into Ecology*. New York: The Viking Press, 1966.

KENDEIGH, S. C., *Animal Ecology*. Englewood Cliffs, N.J.: Prentice-Hall, Inc., 1961.

†KORMONDY, EDWARD J., *Concepts of Ecology*. Englewood Cliffs, N.J.: Prentice-Hall, Inc., 1969.

————, ed., *Readings in Ecology*. Englewood Cliffs, N.J.: Prentice-Hall, Inc., 1965.

†ODUM, EUGENE P., *Ecology*. New York: Holt, Rinehart and Winston, Inc., 1963.

————, *Fundamentals of Ecology* (3rd edn.). Philadelphia: W. B. Saunders Company, 1971.

OOSTING, HENRY J., *The Study of Plant Communities* (2nd edn.). San Francisco: W. H. Freeman Company, 1956.

*REID, KEITH, *Nature's Network*. Garden City, N.Y.: Natural History Press, 1970.

SHELFORD, VICTOR E., *The Ecology of North America*. Urbana, Ill.: University of Illinois Press, 1963.

SMITH, ROBERT L., *Ecology and Field Biology*. New York: Harper & Row, 1966.

*STEPHEN, DAVID, and JAMES LOCKIE, *Nature's Way*. New York: McGraw-Hill Book Company, 1969.

*†STORER, JOHN H., *The Web of Life*. New York: Devin-Adair Company, 1959.

POPULATION, SUCCESSION, ECOSYSTEMS,
AND OTHER ASPECTS OF ECOLOGY

*ALLEN, DURWARD L., *The Life of Prairies and Plains*. New York: McGraw-Hill Book Company, 1967.

*AMOS, WILLIAM H., *The Life of the Pond*. New York: McGraw-Hill Book Company, 1967.

*BERRILL, N. J., *The Life of the Ocean*. New York: McGraw-Hill Book Company, 1966.

†*The Biosphere*. A *Scientific American* book. San Francisco: W. H. Freeman and Company, 1970.

*BROOKS, MAURICE, *The Life of the Mountains*. New York: McGraw-Hill Book Company, 1967.

*ENGEL, LEONARD, and the Editors of *Life*, *The Sea*. New York: Time, Inc., 1961.

ERRINGTON, PAUL, *Of Predation and Life.* Ames, Iowa: Iowa State University Press, 1967.

*FARB, PETER, and the Editors of *Life, The Forest.* New York: Time, Inc., 1963.

*LAUWERYS, J. A., *Man's Impact on Nature.* Garden City, N.Y.: Natural History Press, 1970.

*LEOPOLD, A. STARKER, and the Editors of *Life, The Desert.* New York: Time, Inc., 1961.

†LEOPOLD, ALDO, *A Sand County Almanac.* New York: Oxford University Press, 1966.

*LEY, WILLY, and the Editors of *Life, The Poles.* New York: Time, Inc., 1962.

* McCORMICK, JACK, *The Life of the Forest.* New York: McGraw-Hill Book Company, 1966.

*MILNE, LORUS J. and MARGERY, and the Editors of *Life, The Mountains.* New York: Time, Inc., 1962.

*PRINGLE, LAURENCE, *One Earth, Many People.* New York: The Macmillan Company, 1971.

*†———, *The Only Earth We Have.* New York: The Macmillan Company, 1969.

*PRUITT, WILLIAM O., JR., *Animals of the North.* New York: Harper & Row, 1967.

*RICHARDS, PAUL W., *The Life of the Jungle.* New York: McGraw-Hill Book Company, 1970.

*SUTTON, ANN and MYRON, *The Life of the Desert.* New York: McGraw-Hill Book Company, 1966.

*USINGER, ROBERT L., *The Life of Rivers and Streams.* New York: McGraw-Hill Book Company, 1967.

*WATTS, MAY T., *Reading the Landscape.* New York: The Macmillan Company, 1957.

INDEX

Asterisk indicates drawing, graph, or photograph.

tundra: alpine, 35–36; arctic, 32, *34–*35, 36, 78, 113

veld, *see* grassland
vole, *see* meadow vole

water cycle, *84–85
water pollution, *7, 59–60, 63, 82, 107–108

watershed, 59
weather, effect on populations, 123–124, 126
wolf, 21–22, 40, 121, 125

zebras, *19, 21, 29
zooplankton, 16, 53, 70, 74–75, 80

27538